"After utilizing toolkits from The Art (threats within my organization to which I was completely unaware. Using my team's knowledge as a competitive advantage, we now have superior systems that save time and energy."

"As a new Chief Technology Officer, I was feeling unprepared and inadequate to be successful in my role. I ordered an IT toolkit Sunday night and was prepared Monday morning to shed light on areas of improvement within my organization. I no longer felt overwhelmed and intimidated, I was excited to share what I had learned."

"I used the questionnaires to interview members of my team. I never knew how many insights we could produce collectively with our internal knowledge."

"I usually work until at least 8pm on weeknights. The Art of Service questionnaire saved me so much time and worry that Thursday night I attended my son's soccer game without sacrificing my professional obligations."

"After purchasing The Art of Service toolkit, I was able to identify areas where my company was not in compliance that could have put my job at risk. I looked like a hero when I proactively educated my team on the risks and presented a solid solution."

"I spent months shopping for an external consultant before realizing that The Art of Service would allow my team to consult themselves! Not only did we save time not catching a consultant up to speed, we were able to keep our company information and industry secrets confidential."

"Everyday there are new regulations and processes in my industry. The Art of Service toolkit has kept me ahead by using AI technology to constantly update the toolkits and address emerging needs."

"I customized The Art of Service toolkit to focus specifically on the concerns of my role and industry. I didn't have to waste time with a generic self-help book that wasn't tailored to my exact situation."

"Many of our competitors have asked us about our secret sauce. When I tell them it's the knowledge we have in-house, they never believe me. Little do they know The Art of Service toolkits are working behind the scenes."

"One of my friends hired a consultant who used the knowledge gained working with his company to advise their competitor. Talk about a competitive disadvantage! The Art of Service allowed us to keep our knowledge from walking out the door along with a huge portion of our budget in consulting fees."

"Honestly, I didn't know what I didn't know. Before purchasing The Art of Service, I didn't realize how many areas of my business needed to be refreshed and improved. I am so relieved The Art of Service was there to highlight our blind spots."

"Before The Art of Service, I waited eagerly for consulting company reports to come out each month. These reports kept us up to speed but provided little value because they put our competitors on the same playing field. With The Art of Service, we have uncovered unique insights to drive our business forward."

"Instead of investing extensive resources into an external consultant, we can spend more of our budget towards pursuing our company goals and objectives…while also spending a little more on corporate holiday parties."

"The risk of our competitors getting ahead has been mitigated because The Art of Service has provided us with a 360-degree view of threats within our organization before they even arise."

IBM InfoSphere DataStage
Complete Self-Assessment Guide

Table of Contents

About The Art of Service

The Art of Service, Business Process Architects since 2000, is dedicated to helping stakeholders achieve excellence.

Defining, designing, creating, and implementing a process to solve a stakeholders challenge or meet an objective is the most valuable role… In EVERY group, company, organization and department.

Unless you're talking a one-time, single-use project, there should be a process. Whether that process is managed and implemented by humans, AI, or a combination of the two, it needs to be designed by someone with a complex enough perspective to ask the right questions.

Someone capable of asking the right questions and step back and say, 'What are we really trying to accomplish here? And is there a different way to look at it?'

With The Art of Service's Self-Assessments, we empower people who can do just that — whether their title is marketer, entrepreneur, manager, salesperson, consultant, Business Process Manager, executive assistant, IT Manager, CIO etc... —they are the people who rule the future. They are people who watch the process as it happens, and ask the right questions to make the process work better.

Contact us when you need any support with this Self-Assessment and any help with templates, blue-prints and examples of standard documents you might need:

https://theartofservice.com
support@theartofservice.com

Included Resources - how to access

Included with your purchase of the book is the IBM InfoSphere

DataStage Self-Assessment Spreadsheet Dashboard which contains all questions and Self-Assessment areas and auto-generates insights, graphs, and project RACI planning - all with examples to get you started right away.

How? Simply send an email to
access@theartofservice.com
with this books' title in the subject to get the IBM InfoSphere DataStage Self Assessment Tool right away.

The auto reply will guide you further, you will then receive the following contents with New and Updated specific criteria:

- The latest quick edition of the book in PDF

- The latest complete edition of the book in PDF, which criteria correspond to the criteria in...

- The Self-Assessment Excel Dashboard, and...

- Example pre-filled Self-Assessment Excel Dashboard to get familiar with results generation

- In-depth specific Checklists covering the topic

- Project management checklists and templates to assist with implementation

INCLUDES LIFETIME SELF ASSESSMENT UPDATES

Every self assessment comes with Lifetime Updates and Lifetime Free Updated Books. Lifetime Updates is an industry-first feature which allows you to receive verified self assessment updates, ensuring you always have the most accurate information at your fingertips.

Get it now- you will be glad you did - do it now, before you forget.

Send an email to **access@theartofservice.com** with this books' title in the subject to get the IBM InfoSphere DataStage Self Assessment Tool right away.

Purpose of this Self-Assessment

This Self-Assessment has been developed to improve understanding of the requirements and elements of IBM InfoSphere DataStage, based on best practices and standards in business process architecture, design and quality management.

It is designed to allow for a rapid Self-Assessment to determine how closely existing management practices and procedures correspond to the elements of the Self-Assessment.

The criteria of requirements and elements of IBM InfoSphere DataStage have been rephrased in the format of a Self-Assessment questionnaire, with a seven-criterion scoring system, as explained in this document.

In this format, even with limited background knowledge of IBM InfoSphere DataStage, a manager can quickly review existing operations to determine how they measure up to the standards. This in turn can serve as the starting point of a 'gap analysis' to identify management tools or system elements that might usefully be implemented in the organization to help improve overall performance.

How to use the Self-Assessment

On the following pages are a series of questions to identify to what extent your IBM InfoSphere DataStage initiative is complete in comparison to the requirements set in standards.

To facilitate answering the questions, there is a space in front of each question to enter a score on a scale of '1' to '5'.

1 Strongly Disagree

2 Disagree

3 Neutral

4 Agree

5 Strongly Agree

Read the question and rate it with the following in front of mind:

'In my belief, the answer to this question is clearly defined'.

There are two ways in which you can choose to interpret this statement;
1. how aware are you that the answer to the question is clearly defined
2. for more in-depth analysis you can choose to gather evidence and confirm the answer to the question. This obviously will take more time, most Self-Assessment users opt for the first way to interpret the question and dig deeper later on based on the outcome of the overall Self-Assessment.

A score of '1' would mean that the answer is not clear at all, where a '5' would mean the answer is crystal clear and defined. Leave emtpy when the question is not applicable or you don't want to answer it, you can skip it without affecting your score. Write your score in the space provided.

After you have responded to all the appropriate statements in each section, compute your average score for that section, using the formula provided, and round to the nearest tenth. Then transfer to the corresponding spoke in the IBM InfoSphere DataStage Scorecard on the second next page of the Self-Assessment.

Your completed IBM InfoSphere DataStage Scorecard will give you a clear presentation of which IBM InfoSphere DataStage areas need attention.

IBM InfoSphere DataStage Scorecard Example

Example of how the finalized Scorecard can look like:

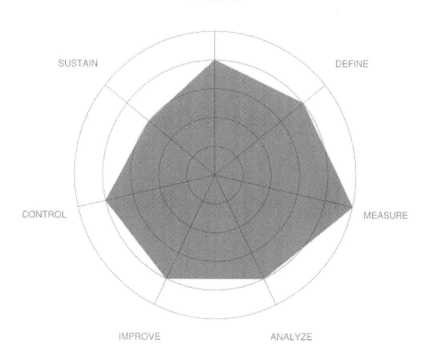

IBM InfoSphere DataStage Scorecard

Your Scores:

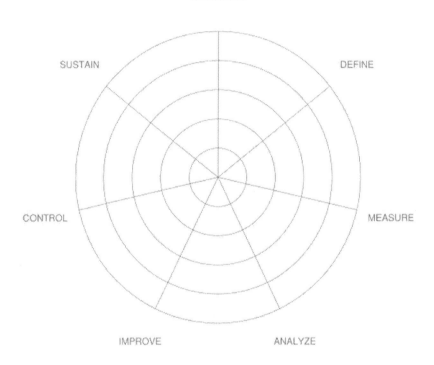

RECOGNIZE

SUSTAIN

DEFINE

CONTROL

MEASURE

IMPROVE

ANALYZE

BEGINNING OF THE SELF-ASSESSMENT:

CRITERION #1: RECOGNIZE

INTENT: Be aware of the need for change. Recognize that there is an unfavorable variation, problem or symptom.

In my belief, the answer to this question is clearly defined:

5 Strongly Agree

4 Agree

3 Neutral

2 Disagree

1 Strongly Disagree

1. What is the maximum number your organization needs to be provisioned?
<--- Score

2. What do you need to know to do load testing in addition to knowing how to use the Load-Runner tool?
<--- Score

3. What levels of issue escalation does your organization expect?

<--- Score

4. As a sponsor, customer or management, how important is it to meet goals, objectives?

<--- Score

5. Who are your key stakeholders who need to sign off?

<--- Score

6. Looking at each person individually – does every one have the qualities which are needed to work in this group?

<--- Score

7. Is the need for organizational change recognized?

<--- Score

8. What are the expected benefits of IBM InfoSphere DataStage to the stakeholder?

<--- Score

9. Is event based rules part of scope?

<--- Score

10. How can project managers and architects determine the level of need for, and potential benefit from, ETL tools?

<--- Score

11. What vendors make products that address the IBM InfoSphere DataStage needs?

<--- Score

12. Who else hopes to benefit from it?
<--- Score

13. What problems are you facing and how do you consider IBM InfoSphere DataStage will circumvent those obstacles?
<--- Score

14. Where is training needed?
<--- Score

15. How does an important issue get so large and so painful without being addressed?
<--- Score

16. Which needs are not included or involved?
<--- Score

17. Are there any specific expectations or concerns about the IBM InfoSphere DataStage team, IBM InfoSphere DataStage itself?
<--- Score

18. Where do you need to exercise leadership?
<--- Score

19. Are problem definition and motivation clearly presented?
<--- Score

20. Do you foresee any need for extracting business rules from legacy systems?
<--- Score

21. Are there IBM InfoSphere DataStage problems defined?

<--- Score

22. What should be considered when identifying available resources, constraints, and deadlines?
<--- Score

23. Which job log message heading identifies the score in the job log?
<--- Score

24. What situation(s) led to this IBM InfoSphere DataStage Self Assessment?
<--- Score

25. What prevents you from making the changes you know will make you a more effective IBM InfoSphere DataStage leader?
<--- Score

26. How are the IBM InfoSphere DataStage's objectives aligned to the group's overall stakeholder strategy?
<--- Score

27. What does IBM InfoSphere DataStage success mean to the stakeholders?
<--- Score

28. Which issues are too important to ignore?
<--- Score

29. Do you need different information or graphics?
<--- Score

30. How have you resolved ETL problems?
<--- Score

31. Are there recognized IBM InfoSphere DataStage problems?
<--- Score

32. How many trainings, in total, are needed?
<--- Score

33. What tools and technologies are needed for a custom IBM InfoSphere DataStage project?
<--- Score

34. Do you need to avoid or amend any IBM InfoSphere DataStage activities?
<--- Score

35. How much are sponsors, customers, partners, stakeholders involved in IBM InfoSphere DataStage? In other words, what are the risks, if IBM InfoSphere DataStage does not deliver successfully?
<--- Score

36. Would you recognize a threat from the inside?
<--- Score

37. Who needs what information?
<--- Score

38. What would happen if IBM InfoSphere DataStage weren't done?
<--- Score

39. Who should resolve the IBM InfoSphere DataStage issues?
<--- Score

40. What are the stakeholder objectives to be achieved with IBM InfoSphere DataStage?
<--- Score

41. What ETL problems have you faced?
<--- Score

42. Are you working on business keys that still need a lookup?
<--- Score

43. What do you need to start doing?
<--- Score

44. What IBM InfoSphere DataStage coordination do you need?
<--- Score

45. What jobs may need investigation?
<--- Score

46. Do you need to expose web services for downstream systems?
<--- Score

47. What is the extent or complexity of the IBM InfoSphere DataStage problem?
<--- Score

48. How many users will need access to the Case Management and Program Integrity tools?
<--- Score

49. What are the symptoms of the problem?
<--- Score

50. How many years of history needs to be available in the archive?

<--- Score

51. Do any other engines have issues?

<--- Score

52. What is the IBM InfoSphere DataStage problem definition? What do you need to resolve?

<--- Score

53. How are you going to measure success?

<--- Score

54. How many simple, moderate and complex predictive models need to be built?

<--- Score

55. Is the quality assurance team identified?

<--- Score

56. Are there issues in accessibility or availability?

<--- Score

57. How much memory space do you need on your system to execute ETL?

<--- Score

58. What extra resources will you need?

<--- Score

59. Are there regulatory / compliance issues?

<--- Score

60. What IBM InfoSphere DataStage capabilities do you need?

<--- Score

61. What methods/protocols does your organization need to be able to support to send and receive files?
<--- Score

62. Will a response program recognize when a crisis occurs and provide some level of response?
<--- Score

63. Does IBM InfoSphere DataStage create potential expectations in other areas that need to be recognized and considered?
<--- Score

64. What are the clients issues and concerns?
<--- Score

65. Consider your own IBM InfoSphere DataStage project, what types of organizational problems do you think might be causing or affecting your problem, based on the work done so far?
<--- Score

Add up total points for this section:
_ _ _ _ _ = Total points for this section

Divided by: _ _ _ _ _ _ (number of statements answered) = _ _ _ _ _ _
Average score for this section

Transfer your score to the IBM InfoSphere DataStage Index at the beginning of the Self-Assessment.

CRITERION #2: DEFINE:

INTENT: Formulate the stakeholder problem. Define the problem, needs and objectives.

In my belief, the answer to this question is clearly defined:

5 Strongly Agree

4 Agree

3 Neutral

2 Disagree

1 Strongly Disagree

1. How did the IBM InfoSphere DataStage manager receive input to the development of a IBM InfoSphere DataStage improvement plan and the estimated completion dates/times of each activity?
<--- Score

2. What are (control) requirements for IBM InfoSphere DataStage Information?
<--- Score

3. Have all of the relationships been defined properly?
<--- Score

4. Is the improvement team aware of the different versions of a process: what they think it is vs. what it actually is vs. what it should be vs. what it could be?
<--- Score

5. What are the boundaries of the scope? What is in bounds and what is not? What is the start point? What is the stop point?
<--- Score

6. How is the team tracking and documenting its work?
<--- Score

7. Does the team have regular meetings?
<--- Score

8. What specifically is the problem? Where does it occur? When does it occur? What is its extent?
<--- Score

9. Are accountability and ownership for IBM InfoSphere DataStage clearly defined?
<--- Score

10. Is there regularly 100% attendance at the team meetings? If not, have appointed substitutes attended to preserve cross-functionality and full representation?
<--- Score

11. Will new user registration be in scope?

<--- Score

12. Has/have the customer(s) been identified?
<--- Score

13. What scope do you want your strategy to cover?
<--- Score

14. Has a project plan, Gantt chart, or similar been developed/completed?
<--- Score

15. What are the dynamics of the communication plan?
<--- Score

16. Are team charters developed?
<--- Score

17. How and when will the baselines be defined?
<--- Score

18. Is the work to date meeting requirements?
<--- Score

19. In what way can you redefine the criteria of choice clients have in your category in your favor?
<--- Score

20. Do the problem and goal statements meet the SMART criteria (specific, measurable, attainable, relevant, and time-bound)?
<--- Score

21. Do you have a IBM InfoSphere DataStage success story or case study ready to tell and share?

<--- Score

22. What are the requirements for audit information?
<--- Score

23. Is there a critical path to deliver IBM InfoSphere DataStage results?
<--- Score

24. Has a team charter been developed and communicated?
<--- Score

25. What information should you gather?
<--- Score

26. Are there different segments of customers?
<--- Score

27. What is in the scope and what is not in scope?
<--- Score

28. How does the IBM InfoSphere DataStage manager ensure against scope creep?
<--- Score

29. Is the IBM InfoSphere DataStage scope complete and appropriately sized?
<--- Score

30. Are different versions of process maps needed to account for the different types of inputs?
<--- Score

31. How will the IBM InfoSphere DataStage team and the group measure complete success of IBM

InfoSphere DataStage?
<--- Score

32. Does your application require that the value of a specific parameter be specified?
<--- Score

33. What investigative case management system do you currently use?
<--- Score

34. Is full participation by members in regularly held team meetings guaranteed?
<--- Score

35. Is IBM InfoSphere DataStage linked to key stakeholder goals and objectives?
<--- Score

36. Are the IBM InfoSphere DataStage requirements testable?
<--- Score

37. When is/was the IBM InfoSphere DataStage start date?
<--- Score

38. Has the direction changed at all during the course of IBM InfoSphere DataStage? If so, when did it change and why?
<--- Score

39. What defines best in class?
<--- Score

40. When are meeting minutes sent out? Who is on

the distribution list?

<--- Score

41. Is IBM InfoSphere DataStage currently on schedule according to the plan?

<--- Score

42. Is the current 'as is' process being followed? If not, what are the discrepancies?

<--- Score

43. What IBM InfoSphere DataStage services do you require?

<--- Score

44. How do you manage changes in IBM InfoSphere DataStage requirements?

<--- Score

45. How often are the team meetings?

<--- Score

46. How will variation in the actual durations of each activity be dealt with to ensure that the expected IBM InfoSphere DataStage results are met?

<--- Score

47. How was the 'as is' process map developed, reviewed, verified and validated?

<--- Score

48. What critical content must be communicated – who, what, when, where, and how?

<--- Score

49. How do you catch IBM InfoSphere DataStage

definition inconsistencies?
<--- Score

50. Has anyone else (internal or external to the group) attempted to solve this problem or a similar one before? If so, what knowledge can be leveraged from these previous efforts?
<--- Score

51. Who are the IBM InfoSphere DataStage improvement team members, including Management Leads and Coaches?
<--- Score

52. Which area of your job design is required to be configured to use the parallel shared container?
<--- Score

53. Is data collected and displayed to better understand customer(s) critical needs and requirements.
<--- Score

54. How many investigators / case workers does your organization have at its disposal?
<--- Score

55. Is the team formed and are team leaders (Coaches and Management Leads) assigned?
<--- Score

56. Are customers identified and high impact areas defined?
<--- Score

57. Is there a IBM InfoSphere DataStage management

charter, including stakeholder case, problem and goal statements, scope, milestones, roles and responsibilities, communication plan?
<--- Score

58. What are the source systems in scope for MDM to consolidate?
<--- Score

59. What is the definition of success?
<--- Score

60. What knowledge or experience is required?
<--- Score

61. Is there a completed SIPOC representation, describing the Suppliers, Inputs, Process, Outputs, and Customers?
<--- Score

62. Have all basic functions of IBM InfoSphere DataStage been defined?
<--- Score

63. Is node adapter redundancy required?
<--- Score

64. Is the team equipped with available and reliable resources?
<--- Score

65. What constraints exist that might impact the team?
<--- Score

66. What happens if IBM InfoSphere DataStage's scope

changes?
<--- Score

67. Is the IBM InfoSphere DataStage scope manageable?
<--- Score

68. Is the team adequately staffed with the desired cross-functionality? If not, what additional resources are available to the team?
<--- Score

69. Has your scope been defined?
<--- Score

70. Are there any constraints known that bear on the ability to perform IBM InfoSphere DataStage work? How is the team addressing them?
<--- Score

71. What are the Roles and Responsibilities for each team member and its leadership? Where is this documented?
<--- Score

72. What is the scope?
<--- Score

73. Has a high-level 'as is' process map been completed, verified and validated?
<--- Score

74. What is software defined storage?
<--- Score

75. Are approval levels defined for contracts and

supplements to contracts?

<--- Score

76. What reports and entitlements are part of the scope?

<--- Score

77. What are the rough order estimates on cost savings/opportunities that IBM InfoSphere DataStage brings?

<--- Score

78. Has the improvement team collected the 'voice of the customer' (obtained feedback – qualitative and quantitative)?

<--- Score

79. What are the ETL implementation Services requirements?

<--- Score

80. What would be the goal or target for a IBM InfoSphere DataStage's improvement team?

<--- Score

81. Are all requirements met?

<--- Score

82. Is the team sponsored by a champion or stakeholder leader?

<--- Score

83. Will team members regularly document their IBM InfoSphere DataStage work?

<--- Score

84. Who is gathering information?

<--- Score

85. Do you all define IBM InfoSphere DataStage in the same way?

<--- Score

86. When is the estimated completion date?

<--- Score

87. Are improvement team members fully trained on IBM InfoSphere DataStage?

<--- Score

88. Have the customer needs been translated into specific, measurable requirements? How?

<--- Score

89. Will team members perform IBM InfoSphere DataStage work when assigned and in a timely fashion?

<--- Score

90. How do you keep key subject matter experts in the loop?

<--- Score

91. Is there a requirement to manage a lot of additional properties along with the value?

<--- Score

92. How do you think the partners involved in IBM InfoSphere DataStage would have defined success?

<--- Score

93. Is there a completed, verified, and validated high-

level 'as is' (not 'should be' or 'could be') stakeholder process map?
<--- Score

94. Is IBM InfoSphere DataStage required?
<--- Score

95. Has the IBM InfoSphere DataStage work been fairly and/or equitably divided and delegated among team members who are qualified and capable to perform the work? Has everyone contributed?
<--- Score

96. Have specific policy objectives been defined?
<--- Score

97. What information do you gather?
<--- Score

98. What is out-of-scope initially?
<--- Score

99. Is system/application administration and infrastructure support part of the scope?
<--- Score

100. What customer feedback methods were used to solicit their input?
<--- Score

101. If substitutes have been appointed, have they been briefed on the IBM InfoSphere DataStage goals and received regular communications as to the progress to date?
<--- Score

102. What are your organizations remote access requirements?

<--- Score

103. Is a fully trained team formed, supported, and committed to work on the IBM InfoSphere DataStage improvements?

<--- Score

104. Does the scope remain the same?

<--- Score

105. Are customer(s) identified and segmented according to their different needs and requirements?

<--- Score

106. Are stakeholder processes mapped?

<--- Score

107. Has everyone on the team, including the team leaders, been properly trained?

<--- Score

108. What key stakeholder process output measure(s) does IBM InfoSphere DataStage leverage and how?

<--- Score

109. What are the compelling stakeholder reasons for embarking on IBM InfoSphere DataStage?

<--- Score

Add up total points for this section:
_ _ _ _ _ = Total points for this section

Divided by: _ _ _ _ _ _ (number of statements answered) = _ _ _ _ _ _

Average score for this section

Transfer your score to the IBM
InfoSphere DataStage Index at the
beginning of the Self-Assessment.

CRITERION #3: MEASURE:

INTENT: Gather the correct data.
Measure the current performance and
evolution of the situation.

In my belief, the answer to this
question is clearly defined:

5 Strongly Agree

4 Agree

3 Neutral

2 Disagree

1 Strongly Disagree

1. How can you measure the performance?
<--- Score

2. Are losses documented, analyzed, and remedial
processes developed to prevent future losses?
<--- Score

3. What users will be impacted?
<--- Score

4. Does management have the right priorities among projects?
<--- Score

5. Do the benefits outweigh the costs?
<--- Score

6. Have you found any 'ground fruit' or 'low-hanging fruit' for immediate remedies to the gap in performance?
<--- Score

7. Are process variation components displayed/communicated using suitable charts, graphs, plots?
<--- Score

8. Have the types of risks that may impact IBM InfoSphere DataStage been identified and analyzed?
<--- Score

9. How does real-time distributed analytics fit into the Big Data challenge?
<--- Score

10. Have all non-recommended alternatives been analyzed in sufficient detail?
<--- Score

11. What details are required of the IBM InfoSphere DataStage cost structure?
<--- Score

12. Is data collected on key measures that were identified?
<--- Score

13. Why is it that other organizations continue to feel an urgency to seek an effective use of analytics?
<--- Score

14. What particular quality tools did the team find helpful in establishing measurements?
<--- Score

15. How do you verify your resources?
<--- Score

16. Which measures and indicators matter?
<--- Score

17. Can you measure the return on analysis?
<--- Score

18. Does your organization provide the historical count of incidents/ problems by priority level?
<--- Score

19. What measurements are possible, practicable and meaningful?
<--- Score

20. Does IBM InfoSphere DataStage analysis isolate the fundamental causes of problems?
<--- Score

21. Do KPIs and metrics link to other business measures?
<--- Score

22. How will users access reports and analytics?

<--- Score

23. How large is the gap between current performance and the customer-specified (goal) performance?
<--- Score

24. Was a data collection plan established?
<--- Score

25. What are the costs?
<--- Score

26. Which costs should be taken into account?
<--- Score

27. What relevant entities could be measured?
<--- Score

28. What measurements are being captured?
<--- Score

29. What are the estimated costs of proposed changes?
<--- Score

30. Who is involved in verifying compliance?
<--- Score

31. What key measures identified indicate the performance of the stakeholder process?
<--- Score

32. Is long term and short term variability accounted for?
<--- Score

33. Is Process Variation Displayed/Communicated?
<--- Score

34. Does the IBM InfoSphere DataStage task fit the client's priorities?
<--- Score

35. What evidence is there and what is measured?
<--- Score

36. Are the measurements objective?
<--- Score

37. What potential environmental factors impact the IBM InfoSphere DataStage effort?
<--- Score

38. Can you do IBM InfoSphere DataStage without complex (expensive) analysis?
<--- Score

39. How will success or failure be measured?
<--- Score

40. What happens if cost savings do not materialize?
<--- Score

41. How long to keep data and how to manage retention costs?
<--- Score

42. What are the currently used analytical software for statistical analysis?
<--- Score

43. What do people want to verify?

<--- Score

44. What is the IBM InfoSphere DataStage business impact?

<--- Score

45. What is the cost of rework?

<--- Score

46. How frequently do you expect data to be refreshed in the analytical tool?

<--- Score

47. How much does it cost?

<--- Score

48. What are your key IBM InfoSphere DataStage organizational performance measures, including key short and longer-term financial measures?

<--- Score

49. What charts has the team used to display the components of variation in the process?

<--- Score

50. What tests verify requirements?

<--- Score

51. What are the characteristics that make a good real-time distributed analytics platform?

<--- Score

52. How sensitive must the IBM InfoSphere DataStage strategy be to cost?

<--- Score

53. What is the right balance of time and resources between investigation, analysis, and discussion and dissemination?

<--- Score

54. How long are analysis results retained?

<--- Score

55. Do you trust that the process transforming and analyzing the data does what it is supposed to do?

<--- Score

56. When a disaster occurs, who gets priority?

<--- Score

57. Is a solid data collection plan established that includes measurement systems analysis?

<--- Score

58. What are the possible causes for ETL run time failures?

<--- Score

59. Is there a Performance Baseline?

<--- Score

60. What could cause delays in the schedule?

<--- Score

61. Why do you expend time and effort to implement measurement, for whom?

<--- Score

62. How do you verify the authenticity of the data and information used?

<--- Score

63. Was a business case (cost/benefit) developed?
<--- Score

64. Is key measure data collection planned
and executed, process variation displayed and
communicated and performance baselined?
<--- Score

65. How will costs be allocated?
<--- Score

66. What could cause you to change course?
<--- Score

**67. Is it going to be a incremental data load or
complete data refresh for the analytical models?**
<--- Score

**68. How does the cloud impact information
governance?**
<--- Score

69. What is an unallowable cost?
<--- Score

70. Are high impact defects defined and identified in
the stakeholder process?
<--- Score

71. Did you tackle the cause or the symptom?
<--- Score

72. How do you quantify and qualify impacts?
<--- Score

73. Does using data in motion reduce your processing costs?

<--- Score

74. How do you pick an appropriate ETL tool or business analytics tool?

<--- Score

75. Are the units of measure consistent?

<--- Score

76. Who should receive measurement reports?

<--- Score

77. What does verifying compliance entail?

<--- Score

78. What are your operating costs?

<--- Score

79. What would be a real cause for concern?

<--- Score

80. Have you made assumptions about the shape of the future, particularly its impact on your customers and competitors?

<--- Score

81. Is the reciprocal of the traditional analysis paradigm appropriate for the business task at hand?

<--- Score

82. Who is responsible for analytics?

<--- Score

83. What type of analysis makes sense to do in real time?

<--- Score

84. What data was collected (past, present, future/ ongoing)?

<--- Score

85. What has the team done to assure the stability and accuracy of the measurement process?

<--- Score

86. Where is it measured?

<--- Score

87. Is customer demographic or geographic data available for new analysis to drive business models?

<--- Score

88. What causes investor action?

<--- Score

89. What will be the data refresh frequency for analytical models?

<--- Score

90. What can be used to verify compliance?

<--- Score

91. What are the key input variables? What are the key process variables? What are the key output variables?

<--- Score

92. Is data collection planned and executed?

<--- Score

93. What are you verifying?
<--- Score

94. What drives O&M cost?
<--- Score

95. Are key measures identified and agreed upon?
<--- Score

96. What are the agreed upon definitions of the high impact areas, defect(s), unit(s), and opportunities that will figure into the process capability metrics?
<--- Score

97. What causes extra work or rework?
<--- Score

98. What is the time period of data that you are looking at for analytics and reporting?
<--- Score

99. What is your cost benefit analysis?
<--- Score

100. What is the total fixed cost?
<--- Score

101. Who participated in the data collection for measurements?
<--- Score

Add up total points for this section:
_ _ _ _ _ = Total points for this section

Divided by: _____ (number of
statements answered) = _____
Average score for this section

Transfer your score to the IBM
InfoSphere DataStage Index at the
beginning of the Self-Assessment.

CRITERION #4: ANALYZE:

INTENT: Analyze causes, assumptions
and hypotheses.

In my belief, the answer to this
question is clearly defined:

5 Strongly Agree

4 Agree

3 Neutral

2 Disagree

1 Strongly Disagree

1. Do you need to involve business owners of the data and report rejected records?
<--- Score

2. Who will facilitate the team and process?
<--- Score

3. Is parallel processing of jobs within the ETL possible?
<--- Score

4. How do you record a data driven test?
<--- Score

5. What is the expected rate of data growth?
<--- Score

6. What tools were used to narrow the list of possible causes?
<--- Score

7. Is there an ETL process or a pre-built cube?
<--- Score

8. What data is required for making determinant business decisions?
<--- Score

9. What data is gathered?
<--- Score

10. What is the purpose of having stored procedures in a database?
<--- Score

11. Are gaps between current performance and the goal performance identified?
<--- Score

12. Are the enterprise metadata reporting needs affecting the development of production environments?
<--- Score

13. Can data be obtained by unauthorized individuals?

<--- Score

14. What is the volume of data load for batch ETL?
<--- Score

15. How much storage is needed to store all that data?
<--- Score

16. Will source data be available day one of the project to be modeled and prepped from Conversion?
<--- Score

17. What is the cost of poor quality as supported by the team's analysis?
<--- Score

18. How long must data be retained by the project?
<--- Score

19. What cobol data type is defined by decimal data within the complex flat file stage?
<--- Score

20. What kind of data are you working with?
<--- Score

21. How does the business use the data?
<--- Score

22. How do you define collaboration and team output?
<--- Score

23. What will be the volume of data to be archived and the frequency of archiving?

<--- Score

24. What organization understands data integration and governance better than IBM?

<--- Score

25. Is your ETL process is really integrable with your business process?

<--- Score

26. Is the current data model sufficient to fulfill the new or updated business requirements?

<--- Score

27. Do you define who is accountable for your corporations Data?

<--- Score

28. What is the correct method to process a file containing multiple record types using a Complex Flat File stage?

<--- Score

29. Can you add value to the current IBM InfoSphere DataStage decision-making process (largely qualitative) by incorporating uncertainty modeling (more quantitative)?

<--- Score

30. How do you parameterize database check points?

<--- Score

31. How do you manually migrate environment

variables for IBM InfoSphere DataStage jobs?
<--- Score

32. What training and qualifications will you need?
<--- Score

**33. Is the current Data Warehouses data robust
enough to support future needs?**
<--- Score

34. When should a process be art not science?
<--- Score

**35. What are the different is manual database
checking types?**
<--- Score

**36. Will there be expectations of a heavy load
related to metadata reporting?**
<--- Score

**37. What are the Key Performance Indicators
around data quality?**
<--- Score

38. What are the processes for audit reporting and
management?
<--- Score

**39. What is driving rapid customer adoption of
data integration grid?**
<--- Score

40. What were the crucial 'moments of truth' on the
process map?
<--- Score

41. Is data assurance in scope for the financial data entities?

<--- Score

42. Have the problem and goal statements been updated to reflect the additional knowledge gained from the analyze phase?

<--- Score

43. Are you using any ETL or Data Integration tool?

<--- Score

44. Is there a Culture of Quality Data in your organization?

<--- Score

45. Does using data in motion solve the problem of getting information from your data faster?

<--- Score

46. Where is the data coming from to measure compliance?

<--- Score

47. What is the current ETL technology used for data integration process?

<--- Score

48. What happens during the ETL process?

<--- Score

49. Did any additional data need to be collected?

<--- Score

50. How can data extraction from dashboards be

automated?

<--- Score

51. What mappings are affected and need to be updated?

<--- Score

52. Are there known qualities about the data to consider?

<--- Score

53. Which data will be required to be loaded into the data warehouse at go live?

<--- Score

54. What is the scenario of when a data refresh is required?

<--- Score

55. How do you need to modify your ongoing ETL process to accommodate data partitioning?

<--- Score

56. Do you need to build simulations using either historical data or theoretical equations?

<--- Score

57. What are the steps of creating a data driven test?

<--- Score

58. Is there a need to migrate historical data?

<--- Score

59. Has an output goal been set?

<--- Score

60. What are the number of tables across each of the data source to be considered?

<--- Score

61. Is your application going to store and work with high data volume?

<--- Score

62. Will you be creating reports from multidimensional data?

<--- Score

63. Where do you need to send the data?

<--- Score

64. Identify an operational issue in your organization, for example, could a particular task be done more quickly or more efficiently by IBM InfoSphere DataStage?

<--- Score

65. What are the change request processes?

<--- Score

66. What processes are used to review, manage, and report exception conditions?

<--- Score

67. How can businesses process tremendous amounts of raw data in an efficient and timely manner to gain actionable insights?

<--- Score

68. How is data used for program management and improvement?

<--- Score

69. Is data and process analysis, root cause analysis and quantifying the gap/opportunity in place?
<--- Score

70. When did the solution start collecting data?
<--- Score

71. How can data be so flawed when it is used by the operational systems?
<--- Score

72. What makes advanced ETL processor different?
<--- Score

73. Which of your data-quality screens consume the most/least time in your ETL window?
<--- Score

74. What are the IBM InfoSphere DataStage design outputs?
<--- Score

75. What is erroneous data in ETL testing?
<--- Score

76. Is the IBM InfoSphere DataStage process severely broken such that a re-design is necessary?
<--- Score

77. What are the different formats in which the historical data is stored in a different source system?
<--- Score

78. Does your organization use imagery for asset data digitization?

<--- Score

79. What process should you select for improvement?

<--- Score

80. What relationships exist between data in different systems?

<--- Score

81. How complex is your ETL process?

<--- Score

82. How did companies get data into new systems?

<--- Score

83. How was the detailed process map generated, verified, and validated?

<--- Score

84. Is there a Data Governance organization set up already?

<--- Score

85. How would business users modify erroneous source data?

<--- Score

86. How will the data be checked for quality?

<--- Score

87. What is the technology of the existing/current data warehouse?

<--- Score

88. How are other organizations Gaining Knowledge From Data?

<--- Score

89. Do you need fine-grained security and sharing settings on your data?

<--- Score

90. What policies are in place to secure personal data?

<--- Score

91. How can data limitations be addressed?

<--- Score

92. Which rule set organizes and moves user data to the correct domains?

<--- Score

93. Is there any way to speed up the process?

<--- Score

94. Is descriptive data coming over from the source properly?

<--- Score

95. Is there any ETL process for getting data from source systems?

<--- Score

96. Who are the business owners of source data?

<--- Score

97. How long does the current ETL process take?

<--- Score

98. Were any designed experiments used to generate additional insight into the data analysis?
<--- Score

99. What is grid computing with infosphere datastage?
<--- Score

100. What are datastage shared containers used for?
<--- Score

101. Which option is required to identify a particular job player processes?
<--- Score

102. What part of the data do you need to process?
<--- Score

103. Are you allowed to use the data?
<--- Score

104. Do you understand your management processes today?
<--- Score

105. What is the process of data transformation required by your system?
<--- Score

106. Is the gap/opportunity displayed and communicated in financial terms?
<--- Score

107. How long do you expect the ETL process to run?

<--- Score

108. What are the file formats for the data for data conversion?
<--- Score

109. What quality tools were used to get through the analyze phase?
<--- Score

110. What is the current tool being used for maintaining the data model?
<--- Score

111. Is ETL a part of data integration engine?
<--- Score

112. What is infosphere datastage server?
<--- Score

113. What conclusions were drawn from the team's data collection and analysis? How did the team reach these conclusions?
<--- Score

114. What is the stewardship process to identify trends or handle exceptions?
<--- Score

115. Are you getting ready to administer database security policies?
<--- Score

116. What are the current data reconciliation and data archival strategies being followed?
<--- Score

117. What is the daily volumes being processed by the current ETL process?

<--- Score

118. Are you using ETL from one or more databases for operational data access?

<--- Score

119. Which data is managed by which system?

<--- Score

120. How many input/output points does it require?

<--- Score

121. Does your organization envision providing providers with access to individual performance data?

<--- Score

122. What tool in DataStage Designer would you use?

<--- Score

123. How will you copy the structure of a table without copying the data?

<--- Score

124. When have you had to focus on data integrity?

<--- Score

125. What about relational databases?

<--- Score

126. How does cleanup affect ETL able data?

<--- Score

127. How much data needs to be online accessible and how much needs to be in archive?
<--- Score

128. What is your current ETL process for moving data?
<--- Score

129. Does the data include all relevant selections or leave out relevant content?
<--- Score

130. How many sources systems will there be for the data warehouse?
<--- Score

131. Did the alleged problems result from clerical errors, bad data integration code, or something else?
<--- Score

132. Were Pareto charts (or similar) used to portray the 'heavy hitters' (or key sources of variation)?
<--- Score

133. What is the master data volume from each of the source systems?
<--- Score

134. What to do About Legacy ETL Processes?
<--- Score

135. How many ETL jobs run to keep systems in sync/bring in external data?

<--- Score

136. What happens to your old InfoSphere DataStage Server jobs?
<--- Score

137. How long did it take to process the job?
<--- Score

138. Have you purchased any complimentary data management solutions through your ETL vendor?
<--- Score

139. Which data integration tools are under consideration?
<--- Score

140. What does the data say about the performance of the stakeholder process?
<--- Score

141. What are the various data quality issues currently being faced?
<--- Score

142. Which job design technique can be used to give unique names to sequential output files that are used in multi-instance jobs?
<--- Score

143. What happens if Apply encounters a data error?
<--- Score

144. What is reference data management?
<--- Score

145. What is the process for rolling out changes?
<--- Score

146. How often will data be collected for measures?
<--- Score

147. Are there currently any challenges with respect to the loading of data?
<--- Score

148. Do you have the authority to produce the output?
<--- Score

149. How do mission and objectives affect the IBM InfoSphere DataStage processes of your organization?
<--- Score

150. Which data should be immediately available, and which might be transferred to cold storage?
<--- Score

151. What resources go in to get the desired output?
<--- Score

152. What qualifies as competition?
<--- Score

153. What systems/processes must you excel at?
<--- Score

154. Do you believe that your ETL process was reliable and valid?
<--- Score

155. How is the quality measured for the current master and reference data?

<--- Score

156. How long is the existing data warehouse expected to be in place?

<--- Score

157. What are the data compliance required?

<--- Score

158. What are the major steps in the ETL process?

<--- Score

159. What is the current data refresh frequency?

<--- Score

160. What data must be processed regardless of policies/rules?

<--- Score

161. What is the current batch window for ETL processing?

<--- Score

162. What is the output?

<--- Score

163. Is data going to need to be transferred over the network?

<--- Score

164. Did any value-added analysis or 'lean thinking' take place to identify some of the gaps shown on the 'as is' process map?

<--- Score

165. Have you ever faced the consequences or poor data quality?

<--- Score

166. What external mappings are affected and need to be updated?

<--- Score

167. What tools were used to generate the list of possible causes?

<--- Score

168. Was a detailed process map created to amplify critical steps of the 'as is' stakeholder process?

<--- Score

169. Which is an advantage of creating a conventional ETL process?

<--- Score

170. How do you map data together for new uses?

<--- Score

171. Has data output been validated?

<--- Score

172. How will corresponding data be collected?

<--- Score

173. When should data be set to disk for safekeeping during the ETL?

<--- Score

174. How to split processing across the different platforms?

<--- Score

175. What are your IBM InfoSphere DataStage processes?
<--- Score

176. Why adopt a hybrid data warehouse approach?
<--- Score

177. Was a cause-and-effect diagram used to explore the different types of causes (or sources of variation)?
<--- Score

178. How is information integrated between InfoSphere DataStage jobs, mappings, and database systems?
<--- Score

179. How do you delete a record from a database?
<--- Score

180. When it comes to data discovery, what lines of inquiry are important?
<--- Score

181. How do you summarize your data quality situation?
<--- Score

182. How is data integrated amongst sub-systems?
<--- Score

183. How will data quality measures be tracked over time?
<--- Score

184. How much historical data is available?

<--- Score

185. How do you know which of the data models must be mapped?

<--- Score

186. Which transformation do you need to perform on your data?

<--- Score

187. What methods do you use to gather IBM InfoSphere DataStage data?

<--- Score

188. What is the difference between a dynamic mapping and a transformation?

<--- Score

189. How can metadata workbench display metadata generated by infosphere discovery?

<--- Score

190. What should your data look like to allow you to use it to optimize your business?

<--- Score

191. What were the financial benefits resulting from any 'ground fruit or low-hanging fruit' (quick fixes)?

<--- Score

192. Why do other organizations Need Reference Data Management?

<--- Score

193. Who is the vendor managing the existing/ current data warehouse?

<--- Score

194. How many years of history data will be migrated to new EDW environment?

<--- Score

195. How many full-time data integration specialists work in your organization?

<--- Score

196. Is an a fast database retrieval rate a testable requirement?

<--- Score

197. Is the data needed for your indicators present in the source systems?

<--- Score

198. What qualifications do IBM InfoSphere DataStage leaders need?

<--- Score

199. Are there errors or warnings with the load process?

<--- Score

200. Where are data picked up or sent to?

<--- Score

201. Are there additional reference files required for encounter processing?

<--- Score

202. What does your Big Data Partner Do for You?

<--- Score

203. What happens if Apply encounters a database error?
<--- Score

204. Have you created database tables?
<--- Score

205. Are there any access governance or recertification processes implemented in the current system?
<--- Score

206. Who owns what data?
<--- Score

207. How must the input data set be organized for input into the Join stage?
<--- Score

208. Will local ETL processes need to create rules for constraints already defined in the MDM system?
<--- Score

209. Will you develop DataStage parallel jobs?
<--- Score

210. Where does the data for calculating the profit margin come from?
<--- Score

211. What is the data refresh frequency?
<--- Score

212. What do you need to build on top of a Mongo database to have a robust search system?
<--- Score

213. Are there any needs for report data access restriction by organization/user?
<--- Score

214. Is your application data centric with storage and retrieval of structured data?
<--- Score

215. How does the server engine define a process?
<--- Score

216. How do you implement and manage your work processes to ensure that they meet design requirements?
<--- Score

217. What kind/format of geospatial datasets does your organization require?
<--- Score

218. Is the performance gap determined?
<--- Score

219. Have any additional benefits been identified that will result from closing all or most of the gaps?
<--- Score

220. Where does the data in a data mart come from?
<--- Score

221. What is new -- what is next in Data

Integration?

<--- Score

222. Do the underlying databases exist, enabling a DSS to be constructed?

<--- Score

223. What is the ETL processing window?

<--- Score

224. Where does the data go to, and how is it transformed?

<--- Score

225. How quickly do you process the data to generate actionable information?

<--- Score

226. What are your outputs?

<--- Score

227. Where does the data come from, and how is it transformed?

<--- Score

228. Who is involved with workflow mapping?

<--- Score

229. What happens to the data when constraints are implemented?

<--- Score

230. What is the current ETL processing window?

<--- Score

231. What role must a user have to delete shared

metadata assets from the repository?

<--- Score

232. Will it able to support the growth rate of your enterprise wide Data volume for a considerable long span of time?

<--- Score

233. Is a a fast database retrieval rate a testable requirement?

<--- Score

234. Why else would your organization put that data through so many quality control processes?

<--- Score

235. What data volumes are you going to manipulate?

<--- Score

236. How much efficient is it to bring dirty data in shape?

<--- Score

237. What changed with the advent of Big Data?

<--- Score

238. Think about some of the processes you undertake within your organization, which do you own?

<--- Score

239. What does your current data integration infrastructure look like?

<--- Score

240. How does the organization define, manage, and improve its IBM InfoSphere DataStage processes?
<--- Score

241. Where will data transformation / quality processes run?
<--- Score

242. Do you have previous relational database experience?
<--- Score

243. How are data elements and objects related to each other?
<--- Score

244. What problems will eventually drive you to replace your current primary data integration platform?
<--- Score

245. Are temporary data elements to be included at a later date?
<--- Score

246. Are there any resource/time constraints for ETL processes?
<--- Score

247. What is datastage/quality stage administrator client used for?
<--- Score

248. Are you allowed to collect the data?
<--- Score

249. What did the team gain from developing a sub-process map?
<--- Score

250. What will drive IBM InfoSphere DataStage change?
<--- Score

251. What are the characteristics of big data?
<--- Score

252. How to test database in manually?
<--- Score

253. Is end to end Data Governance Methodology establishment in scope?
<--- Score

254. What do you know about your data?
<--- Score

255. Does the vendor have the tools to clean the data or does your organization need to develop the tools?
<--- Score

256. What are the flat sequential files in the data stream?
<--- Score

257. Is it well parsed or commingled data or domains?
<--- Score

258. How is datastage table metadata shared among datastage projects?

<--- Score

259. What internal processes need improvement?
<--- Score

260. Were there any improvement opportunities identified from the process analysis?
<--- Score

261. Which command is required to check the datastage job status?
<--- Score

262. How can data caching have a negative effect on load testing results?
<--- Score

263. Are the correct data sources being used for measuring success?
<--- Score

264. How else could you know which other attributes to add to the data model?
<--- Score

265. Does the enterprise require metadata reporting?
<--- Score

266. How is it being processed and used?
<--- Score

267. Is referential integrity designed into the database or in the application?
<--- Score

268. What price tag would you place on the value of truly understanding the data sources of your data-driven project?
<--- Score

269. How is the Metadata Repository populated with DataStage jobs runtime information?
<--- Score

270. Is the stored procedure returning data using DB2 result sets?
<--- Score

271. What are the Service Level Agreements and/ or performance goals required for encounter processing?
<--- Score

272. Will users be sharing metadata to perform tasks?
<--- Score

273. When are constraints to the data applied?
<--- Score

274. Do you, as a leader, bounce back quickly from setbacks?
<--- Score

275. Who is involved in the management review process?
<--- Score

276. What IBM InfoSphere DataStage data will be collected?
<--- Score

277. Is that the sole source of data?

<--- Score

278. How many records were processed?

<--- Score

279. What are the revised rough estimates of the financial savings/opportunity for IBM InfoSphere DataStage improvements?

<--- Score

280. Does your organization use LiDAR for data collection?

<--- Score

281. What you normally check for in the Database Testing?

<--- Score

282. What metrics tie to KPIs and to what data are the metrics applied?

<--- Score

283. What IBM InfoSphere DataStage data should be managed?

<--- Score

284. Which type of data can be extracted using the Unstructured Data stage?

<--- Score

285. Are the data of sufficient quality for your research purposes?

<--- Score

286. Do you have all the data needed to test the complex ETL routines?

<--- Score

Add up total points for this section:
_ _ _ _ _ = Total points for this section

Divided by: _ _ _ _ _ _ (number of statements answered) = _ _ _ _ _ _ Average score for this section

Transfer your score to the IBM InfoSphere DataStage Index at the beginning of the Self-Assessment.

CRITERION #5: IMPROVE:

INTENT: Develop a practical solution. Innovate, establish and test the solution and to measure the results.

In my belief, the answer to this question is clearly defined:

5 Strongly Agree

4 Agree

3 Neutral

2 Disagree

1 Strongly Disagree

1. How can you improve performance?
<--- Score

2. What assumptions are made about the solution and approach?
<--- Score

3. Which MDM solution are you implementing?
<--- Score

4. What attendant changes will need to be made to ensure that the solution is successful?
<--- Score

5. Is the optimal solution selected based on testing and analysis?
<--- Score

6. Are events managed to resolution?
<--- Score

7. Is the solution or any of its content under any current Legal hold?
<--- Score

8. How does your organization evaluate strategic IBM InfoSphere DataStage success?
<--- Score

9. Who manages supplier risk management in your organization?
<--- Score

10. Is a solution implementation plan established, including schedule/work breakdown structure, resources, risk management plan, cost/budget, and control plan?
<--- Score

11. Are the most efficient solutions problem-specific?
<--- Score

12. Are improved process ('should be') maps modified based on pilot data and analysis?
<--- Score

13. What are the implications of the one critical IBM InfoSphere DataStage decision 10 minutes, 10 months, and 10 years from now?
<--- Score

14. What alternative responses are available to manage risk?
<--- Score

15. Who controls the risk?
<--- Score

16. Where do the IBM InfoSphere DataStage decisions reside?
<--- Score

17. What are the concrete IBM InfoSphere DataStage results?
<--- Score

18. Will your organization provide guidance on the development of measures and metrics?
<--- Score

19. What tools were used to evaluate the potential solutions?
<--- Score

20. Are procedures documented for managing IBM InfoSphere DataStage risks?
<--- Score

21. What tools were used to tap into the creativity and encourage 'outside the box' thinking?
<--- Score

22. Is information server on Hadoop using map/reduce?

<--- Score

23. What are the affordable IBM InfoSphere DataStage risks?

<--- Score

24. What is IBM InfoSphere DataStage risk?

<--- Score

25. What is the single sign-on solution employed by your organization?

<--- Score

26. How do you improve IBM InfoSphere DataStage service perception, and satisfaction?

<--- Score

27. Describe the design of the pilot and what tests were conducted, if any?

<--- Score

28. What communications are necessary to support the implementation of the solution?

<--- Score

29. Is there a small-scale pilot for proposed improvement(s)? What conclusions were drawn from the outcomes of a pilot?

<--- Score

30. Is the scope clearly documented?

<--- Score

31. When you map the key players in your own work and the types/domains of relationships with them, which relationships do you find easy and which challenging, and why?
<--- Score

32. Are possible solutions generated and tested?
<--- Score

33. Are risk management tasks balanced centrally and locally?
<--- Score

34. What is the magnitude of the improvements?
<--- Score

35. What has been your approach to delivering results to the business?
<--- Score

36. What can you do to improve?
<--- Score

37. Is IBM InfoSphere DataStage documentation maintained?
<--- Score

38. What are the IBM InfoSphere DataStage security risks?
<--- Score

39. What do you want to improve?
<--- Score

40. Who controls key decisions that will be made?
<--- Score

41. Was a pilot designed for the proposed solution(s)?
<--- Score

42. How will you measure the results?
<--- Score

43. Which IBM InfoSphere DataStage solution is appropriate?
<--- Score

44. Is pilot data collected and analyzed?
<--- Score

45. How do you link measurement and risk?
<--- Score

46. Is information shared with other application solutions?
<--- Score

47. What were the underlying assumptions on the cost-benefit analysis?
<--- Score

48. How do you ensure collaboration across your development ecosystem?
<--- Score

49. Are new and improved process ('should be') maps developed?
<--- Score

50. Are the key business and technology risks being managed?
<--- Score

51. How does the solution remove the key sources of issues discovered in the analyze phase?
<--- Score

52. Does a good decision guarantee a good outcome?
<--- Score

53. Who are the IBM InfoSphere DataStage decision-makers?
<--- Score

54. How do you measure progress and evaluate training effectiveness?
<--- Score

55. What IBM InfoSphere DataStage improvements can be made?
<--- Score

56. Can you integrate quality management and risk management?
<--- Score

57. At what point will vulnerability assessments be performed once IBM InfoSphere DataStage is put into production (e.g., ongoing Risk Management after implementation)?
<--- Score

58. Who are the IBM InfoSphere DataStage decision makers?
<--- Score

59. How do you improve productivity?
<--- Score

60. What lessons, if any, from a pilot were incorporated into the design of the full-scale solution?
<--- Score

61. Is there a cost/benefit analysis of optimal solution(s)?
<--- Score

62. What are your current levels and trends in key measures or indicators of workforce and leader development?
<--- Score

63. Are the best solutions selected?
<--- Score

64. Is the IBM InfoSphere DataStage solution sustainable?
<--- Score

65. What is the team's contingency plan for potential problems occurring in implementation?
<--- Score

66. Were any criteria developed to assist the team in testing and evaluating potential solutions?
<--- Score

67. How is knowledge sharing about risk management improved?
<--- Score

68. How many years of history must be available in the solution online?
<--- Score

69. Who are the people involved in developing and implementing IBM InfoSphere DataStage?

<--- Score

70. What criteria will you use to assess your IBM InfoSphere DataStage risks?

<--- Score

71. Risk events: what are the things that could go wrong?

<--- Score

72. Is there any other IBM InfoSphere DataStage solution?

<--- Score

73. What is the implementation plan?

<--- Score

74. Are you implementing a physical MDM solution?

<--- Score

75. What would happen to your business results if you make a particular change?

<--- Score

76. What are the best opportunities for value improvement?

<--- Score

77. Are there any constraints (technical, political, cultural, or otherwise) that would inhibit certain solutions?

<--- Score

78. What risks do you need to manage?
<--- Score

79. Is a contingency plan established?
<--- Score

80. Are modern tools available that make development easier?
<--- Score

81. What needs improvement? Why?
<--- Score

82. How does pricing affect your ETL purchasing decision?
<--- Score

83. Do you have the optimal project management team structure?
<--- Score

84. How do you deal with IBM InfoSphere DataStage risk?
<--- Score

85. How will the team or the process owner(s) monitor the implementation plan to see that it is working as intended?
<--- Score

86. What does the 'should be' process map/design look like?
<--- Score

87. Do the viable solutions scale to future needs?

<--- Score

88. Is risk periodically assessed?
<--- Score

89. What error proofing will be done to address some of the discrepancies observed in the 'as is' process?
<--- Score

90. How many users of each type will there be in the new solution?
<--- Score

91. How is continuous improvement applied to risk management?
<--- Score

92. Do you need to do a usability evaluation?
<--- Score

93. How will the group know that the solution worked?
<--- Score

94. To what extent does management recognize IBM InfoSphere DataStage as a tool to increase the results?
<--- Score

95. What is IBM InfoSphere DataStage's impact on utilizing the best solution(s)?
<--- Score

96. Has the job profile been optimized?
<--- Score

97. Do you need to understand and customize the

underlying solution?

<--- Score

98. What tools were most useful during the improve phase?

<--- Score

99. How do you speed development through common models and policies?

<--- Score

100. How did the team generate the list of possible solutions?

<--- Score

101. Will offshore resources be allowed for application and infrastructure development and support?

<--- Score

102. Is the implementation plan designed?

<--- Score

103. How do you better understand the current quality and status of your reports?

<--- Score

104. Do you need to create scorecarding solutions?

<--- Score

105. Are there any preferences in terms of Products/tools for Case Management Solution?

<--- Score

106. How do you measure improved IBM InfoSphere DataStage service perception, and satisfaction?

<--- Score

107. Are the risks fully understood, reasonable and manageable?
<--- Score

Add up total points for this section:
_ _ _ _ _ = Total points for this section

Divided by: _ _ _ _ _ _ (number of
statements answered) = _ _ _ _ _ _
Average score for this section

Transfer your score to the IBM
InfoSphere DataStage Index at the
beginning of the Self-Assessment.

CRITERION #6: CONTROL:

INTENT: Implement the practical solution. Maintain the performance and correct possible complications.

In my belief, the answer to this question is clearly defined:

5 Strongly Agree

4 Agree

3 Neutral

2 Disagree

1 Strongly Disagree

1. Will any special training be provided for results interpretation?
<--- Score

2. Is there documentation that will support the successful operation of the improvement?
<--- Score

3. What are the critical parameters to watch?

<--- Score

4. Does job training on the documented procedures need to be part of the process team's education and training?
<--- Score

5. Has the improved process and its steps been standardized?
<--- Score

6. Where does the Alert Monitor get information?
<--- Score

7. Is there a standardized process?
<--- Score

8. Does the IBM InfoSphere DataStage performance meet the customer's requirements?
<--- Score

9. Is there a control plan in place for sustaining improvements (short and long-term)?
<--- Score

10. Is the custom data object related to standard data, or is it independent?
<--- Score

11. How will the day-to-day responsibilities for monitoring and continual improvement be transferred from the improvement team to the process owner?
<--- Score

12. Are operating procedures consistent?

<--- Score

13. What are the future activities planned for the ETL/BI application?
<--- Score

14. Act/Adjust: What Do you Need to Do Differently?
<--- Score

15. What enables the controller and the host to communicate with each other in Load Runner?
<--- Score

16. What do you measure to verify effectiveness gains?
<--- Score

17. What data accuracy standard does your organization use for collecting assets?
<--- Score

18. Is a response plan in place for when the input, process, or output measures indicate an 'out-of-control' condition?
<--- Score

19. What are the key elements of your IBM InfoSphere DataStage performance improvement system, including your evaluation, organizational learning, and innovation processes?
<--- Score

20. When do you plan to replace your current primary data integration platform?
<--- Score

21. Does the response plan contain a definite closed loop continual improvement scheme (e.g., plan-do-check-act)?

<--- Score

22. Have new or revised work instructions resulted?

<--- Score

23. What is the control/monitoring plan?

<--- Score

24. How do you configure which Discovery Server is monitored by a Discovery Engine Service?

<--- Score

25. How will the process owner verify improvement in present and future sigma levels, process capabilities?

<--- Score

26. Is there a recommended audit plan for routine surveillance inspections of IBM InfoSphere DataStage's gains?

<--- Score

27. How will input, process, and output variables be checked to detect for sub-optimal conditions?

<--- Score

28. Who has control over resources?

<--- Score

29. How can you best use all of your knowledge repositories to enhance learning and sharing?

<--- Score

30. How might the group capture best practices and

lessons learned so as to leverage improvements?
<--- Score

31. How is IBM InfoSphere DataStage project cost planned, managed, monitored?
<--- Score

32. What are the open standard formats that are required for exporting the data from source system to ETL?
<--- Score

33. What is the best design framework for IBM InfoSphere DataStage organization now that, in a post industrial-age if the top-down, command and control model is no longer relevant?
<--- Score

34. Are there documented procedures?
<--- Score

35. Are new process steps, standards, and documentation ingrained into normal operations?
<--- Score

36. How should project managers, architects and vendors plan for the convergence of ETL with other styles of integration technology?
<--- Score

37. Do you monitor the effectiveness of your IBM InfoSphere DataStage activities?
<--- Score

38. Are documented procedures clear and easy to follow for the operators?

<--- Score

39. Is there a transfer of ownership and knowledge to process owner and process team tasked with the responsibilities.
<--- Score

40. Who is the IBM InfoSphere DataStage process owner?
<--- Score

41. How will the process owner and team be able to hold the gains?
<--- Score

42. What key inputs and outputs are being measured on an ongoing basis?
<--- Score

43. What other systems, operations, processes, and infrastructures (hiring practices, staffing, training, incentives/rewards, metrics/dashboards/scorecards, etc.) need updates, additions, changes, or deletions in order to facilitate knowledge transfer and improvements?
<--- Score

44. What other areas of the group might benefit from the IBM InfoSphere DataStage team's improvements, knowledge, and learning?
<--- Score

45. Is knowledge gained on process shared and institutionalized?
<--- Score

46. Are suggested corrective/restorative actions indicated on the response plan for known causes to problems that might surface?
<--- Score

47. Is new knowledge gained imbedded in the response plan?
<--- Score

48. What is the recommended frequency of auditing?
<--- Score

49. What should the next improvement project be that is related to IBM InfoSphere DataStage?
<--- Score

50. Is a response plan established and deployed?
<--- Score

51. How will report readings be checked to effectively monitor performance?
<--- Score

52. What files and folders must be monitored?
<--- Score

53. Can you adapt and adjust to changing IBM InfoSphere DataStage situations?
<--- Score

54. Are controls in place and consistently applied?
<--- Score

55. How will new or emerging customer needs/ requirements be checked/communicated to orient the process toward meeting the new specifications

and continually reducing variation?

<--- Score

56. What are the known security controls?

<--- Score

57. How do you establish and deploy modified action plans if circumstances require a shift in plans and rapid execution of new plans?

<--- Score

58. Is there a documented and implemented monitoring plan?

<--- Score

59. What quality tools were useful in the control phase?

<--- Score

60. Who sets the IBM InfoSphere DataStage standards?

<--- Score

61. What types of actions must be monitored?

<--- Score

62. What should you measure to verify efficiency gains?

<--- Score

63. What are your organizations plans to adopt Business intelligence software?

<--- Score

64. Does a troubleshooting guide exist or is it needed?

<--- Score

65. Is reporting being used or needed?
<--- Score

Add up total points for this section:
_____ = Total points for this section

Divided by: _____ (number of
statements answered) = _____
Average score for this section

Transfer your score to the IBM
InfoSphere DataStage Index at the
beginning of the Self-Assessment.

CRITERION #7: SUSTAIN:

INTENT: Retain the benefits.

In my belief, the answer to this question is clearly defined:

5 Strongly Agree

4 Agree

3 Neutral

2 Disagree

1 Strongly Disagree

1. Do you want users of the feed to look up information only?
<--- Score

2. What is the currently utilized ETL tool?
<--- Score

3. How many will avoid past mistakes made with ETL and ensure that a short-term strategy is backed by longer-term possibilities?
<--- Score

4. What is the level of system loading expected to occur during specific business scenario?
<--- Score

5. How integrated is the ETL tool with other tools in the suite?
<--- Score

6. How can it be accessed and by whom?
<--- Score

7. What are the different Reporting and ETL tools available in the market?
<--- Score

8. What meaning does it have to the business?
<--- Score

9. How often is information exchanged?
<--- Score

10. Is the price tag for the ETL Tool manageable with your IT budget?
<--- Score

11. How many providers are there in your provider file?
<--- Score

12. Are the ETL jobs expected to run as batch or real-time?
<--- Score

13. Why and what is the IMS Catalog?
<--- Score

14. What is the current level of support provided for the ETL and BI application?

<--- Score

15. Do you provide customized ETL functionality?

<--- Score

16. What is your formula for success in IBM InfoSphere DataStage ?

<--- Score

17. Which archive version is correct?

<--- Score

18. How do you ensure ETL conventions are followed?

<--- Score

19. How are products on the ETL assessed?

<--- Score

20. What ETL tools are in use in your environment?

<--- Score

21. What are you trying to prove to yourself, and how might it be hijacking your life and business success?

<--- Score

22. What are the key business elements to address?

<--- Score

23. How can the extracted information be transformed and quality assured?

<--- Score

24. Who is responsible for ensuring appropriate resources (time, people and money) are allocated to IBM InfoSphere DataStage?
<--- Score

25. What tools are used to manage the ETL?
<--- Score

26. How to derive a set of typical structural patterns for an ETL scenario?
<--- Score

27. Are there multiple parts or conditions to the validation?
<--- Score

28. Do you make a change without breaking the consistent model?
<--- Score

29. How did infosphere discovery find rows?
<--- Score

30. How do you stay inspired?
<--- Score

31. Where is load testing usually done?
<--- Score

32. Which technologies are covered by the ETL?
<--- Score

33. What is running and what are the most recently completed jobs?
<--- Score

34. Which ETL tools will be used in order to build the dw?

<--- Score

35. How many end users you have in the reporting platform?

<--- Score

36. What are the sweet spots of information?

<--- Score

37. Which products are installed on the source?

<--- Score

38. Do other factors affect the day, time, and duration ingest constraints?

<--- Score

39. Which actions are available when editing a message handler?

<--- Score

40. How to handle tables with referential integrity?

<--- Score

41. What is the best ETL tool for your organization?

<--- Score

42. What criteria would you use to select Web transactions for load testing?

<--- Score

43. What, if any, ETL tools does your organization currently use?

<--- Score

44. Is there a lifecycle to the information?
<--- Score

45. What is your IBM InfoSphere DataStage strategy?
<--- Score

46. Is it a completely separate key added during ETL?
<--- Score

47. What are the technologies that the ETL components have to connect to?
<--- Score

48. How many instances of the Sequential File stage will run in parallel?
<--- Score

49. What are the usability implications of IBM InfoSphere DataStage actions?
<--- Score

50. Have benefits been optimized with all key stakeholders?
<--- Score

51. Is it a packaged application or something that was custom built?
<--- Score

52. What does an ETL Architect in your organization do?
<--- Score

53. Which client tool is used to export environment

variables from a project?

<--- Score

54. Is there a minimum number of previous clients your organization expects to see?

<--- Score

55. Do you have a preferred ETL toolset?

<--- Score

56. What is your Middleware / ETL strategy?

<--- Score

57. What type of activities should be blocked?

<--- Score

58. What will be your approach if a particular script in Load Test fails?

<--- Score

59. What do you do with a Spatial ETL Tool?

<--- Score

60. How do you use a different repository with the Discovery Server?

<--- Score

61. Which technique method would be the most efficient to create a globally sorted target sequential file?

<--- Score

62. How do you edit the configuration file for the Discovery Server or Discovery Engine Service?

<--- Score

63. How do you start a Streams application job?
<--- Score

64. What version of IBM InfoSphere Information Server are you using?
<--- Score

65. Do any of the ETL/BI applications have more than one version deployed?
<--- Score

66. What is the name on the Incumbent organization?
<--- Score

67. Think of your IBM InfoSphere DataStage project, what are the main functions?
<--- Score

68. What can go wrong without integration?
<--- Score

69. Do you think IBM InfoSphere DataStage accomplishes the goals you expect it to accomplish?
<--- Score

70. What role does communication play in the success or failure of a IBM InfoSphere DataStage project?
<--- Score

71. Do you feel that more should be done in the IBM InfoSphere DataStage area?
<--- Score

72. How many products are Listed on the ETL?
<--- Score

73. How do you proactively clarify deliverables and IBM InfoSphere DataStage quality expectations?

<--- Score

74. What type of information can safely be ignored?

<--- Score

75. Which tables or files were read from or written to?

<--- Score

76. Are any tables marked as reference tables?

<--- Score

77. Who will determine interim and final deadlines?

<--- Score

78. What is ibm infosphere information server?

<--- Score

79. Which tools, technologies and/or approaches do you use for ETL and which make sense for any given application?

<--- Score

80. How do you configure which Discovery Server your Discovery Studio is connected to?

<--- Score

81. Do you have any maintenance applied?

<--- Score

82. What is next for updating users/apps?

<--- Score

83. What are the differences between technical and business errors?

<--- Score

84. What are various ETL tools available in the market?

<--- Score

85. Is your basic point _____ or _____?

<--- Score

86. Are there aspects to the rule that involve the statistics from the validation?

<--- Score

87. What happens if you do not have enough funding?

<--- Score

88. How can spatial and non-spatial information be extracted and combined?

<--- Score

89. What is your environment capacity?

<--- Score

90. What message handler level is available?

<--- Score

91. Marketing budgets are tighter, consumers are more skeptical, and social media has changed forever the way we talk about IBM InfoSphere DataStage, how do you gain traction?

<--- Score

92. Is the user, password, and connection string combination correct?

<--- Score

93. How will the cluster be connected into the existing clients infrastructure?

<--- Score

94. When did the job run start and when did it complete?

<--- Score

95. Does your organization provide historical average counts of Help Desk contacts/interactions per month?

<--- Score

96. Do guest users have a higher propensity to buy versus browse?

<--- Score

97. What are ETL tester responsibilities?

<--- Score

98. How do you cross-sell and up-sell your IBM InfoSphere DataStage success?

<--- Score

99. How many cots/small custom build applications currently exist?

<--- Score

100. How long will it take to change?

<--- Score

101. What does the acronym ETL stand for?

<--- Score

102. How to negotiate with ETL tool vendors?
<--- Score

103. How effective the ETL Tool for Integration purpose?
<--- Score

104. What are the basic checks done during ETL Testing?
<--- Score

105. Who is responsible for IBM InfoSphere DataStage?
<--- Score

106. What are your organizations software and hardware technology refresh expectations?
<--- Score

107. Does your organization stipulate an acceptable time for system response to a user request for information?
<--- Score

108. What would have to be true for the option on the table to be the best possible choice?
<--- Score

109. Is maximizing IBM InfoSphere DataStage protection the same as minimizing IBM InfoSphere DataStage loss?
<--- Score

110. Who is going to spread your message?

<--- Score

111. What technologies are listed on the ETL?
<--- Score

112. Are all of the ETL jobs running?
<--- Score

113. How are KPIs and metrics communicated?
<--- Score

114. How many instances of the Sequential File stage will run?
<--- Score

115. Are you relevant? Will you be relevant five years from now? Ten?
<--- Score

116. When was the last time it was updated?
<--- Score

117. How important is IBM InfoSphere DataStage to the user organizations mission?
<--- Score

118. What are current IBM InfoSphere DataStage paradigms?
<--- Score

119. What is the kind of project structure that would be appropriate for your IBM InfoSphere DataStage project, should it be formal and complex, or can it be less formal and relatively simple?
<--- Score

120. Are there any SLAs around the ETL jobs to be completed?

<--- Score

121. What is the setup up of your organizations network infrastructure?

<--- Score

122. What is the end user satisfaction level with current reports?

<--- Score

123. How is user access currently managed?

<--- Score

124. What type of activity should prompt alerts?

<--- Score

125. Can ETL error logs be automatically emailed?

<--- Score

126. Does the enterprise have a large, intricate glossary?

<--- Score

127. How many member eligibility feeds are there in source systems?

<--- Score

128. What type of changes should be reported?

<--- Score

129. What are specific IBM InfoSphere DataStage rules to follow?

<--- Score

130. Will other systems have to be discontinued?

<--- Score

131. Who can use the Configuration and Management Components?

<--- Score

132. Which will lead to the best run time performance?

<--- Score

133. Who do you want your customers to become?

<--- Score

134. What is information services director?

<--- Score

135. How do you decide how much to remunerate an employee?

<--- Score

136. How much coding effort is reduced with the use of the ETL Tool?

<--- Score

137. How do you configure which Discovery Engine Service will run your Discovery Studio tasks?

<--- Score

138. What kind of ROI do other organizations see from BI and PM deployments?

<--- Score

139. Which systems are best sources for specific pieces of information?

<--- Score

140. How many tables to be considered as volume to be handled as part of ETL activities?
<--- Score

141. What ETL technology will be used?
<--- Score

142. Is the IBM InfoSphere DataStage organization completing tasks effectively and efficiently?
<--- Score

143. Do you have to have traceability information visualized?
<--- Score

144. Are there any activities that you can take off your to do list?
<--- Score

145. What kind of programming skill is available in your organization?
<--- Score

146. What is it like to work for you?
<--- Score

147. What machine model, operating system, and version are running?
<--- Score

148. What are the different scenarios of ETL run?
<--- Score

149. Will the implementation Services include any

additional ETL jobs?

<--- Score

150. What was the context?

<--- Score

151. When do you enter connection info?

<--- Score

152. What is effective IBM InfoSphere DataStage?

<--- Score

153. How is the user provisioning currently handled?

<--- Score

154. How do you load and unload a compile module?

<--- Score

155. Are there any archive actions being used?

<--- Score

156. Is there currently a user support helpdesk?

<--- Score

157. What was the impetus for starting the project and what are its goals?

<--- Score

158. How many users do you emulate with Load-Runner on a PC?

<--- Score

159. Is the primary diagnosis code appropriate and valid for the service performed?

<--- Score

160. What information domains are you looking to better govern?
<--- Score

161. What is the source of the information?
<--- Score

162. How can you incorporate support to ensure safe and effective use of IBM InfoSphere DataStage into the services that you provide?
<--- Score

163. How many tables to be considered as volume to be handled as part of ETL source systems?
<--- Score

164. What are the major differences between Stress testing, Load testing, Volume testing?
<--- Score

165. How do you choose which architectures to deploy for your particular situation?
<--- Score

166. How does IBM InfoSphere DataStage integrate with other stakeholder initiatives?
<--- Score

167. What should a proof of concept or pilot accomplish?
<--- Score

168. Where does the single version of the truth reside in the warehouse?

<--- Score

169. Why use the ETL Acceleration Suite?
<--- Score

170. What inferences should be made available to other users and in what form?
<--- Score

171. How is your business performing?
<--- Score

172. How many partitions will your catalog have?
<--- Score

173. What has been left out from ETL?
<--- Score

174. Is there a way to show that a product is listed on the ETL?
<--- Score

175. Is the impact that IBM InfoSphere DataStage has shown?
<--- Score

176. Which tools are best for enterprise ETL?
<--- Score

177. What are your most important goals for the strategic IBM InfoSphere DataStage objectives?
<--- Score

178. What is your BATNA (best alternative to a negotiated agreement)?
<--- Score

179. What is the current product used for ETL, Reports and EDW?
<--- Score

180. When would your organization accept partial recovery?
<--- Score

181. What are the key price and performance metrics of ETL in the cloud?
<--- Score

182. How much interruption does your business tolerate?
<--- Score

183. Does the source topology include multiple engine tiers?
<--- Score

184. What should you look for in an ETL Tool?
<--- Score

185. Will real time loading be included?
<--- Score

186. Were lessons learned captured and communicated?
<--- Score

187. Do you currently use an ETL tool?
<--- Score

188. Are there any existing ETL and scheduling tool currently used?

<--- Score

189. Has the job been executing consistently?
<--- Score

190. What kinds of maintenance windows will your organization find acceptable?
<--- Score

191. How are you doing compared to your industry?
<--- Score

192. What are your personal philosophies regarding IBM InfoSphere DataStage and how do they influence your work?
<--- Score

193. What are the short and long-term IBM InfoSphere DataStage goals?
<--- Score

194. Is the current staffing level adequate?
<--- Score

195. Which capability does business lineage provide?
<--- Score

196. Will there be any necessary staff changes (redundancies or new hires)?
<--- Score

197. Does your organization provide historical average counts of service desk contacts/ interactions per month?
<--- Score

198. How often will the projects be backed up?
<--- Score

199. Where does blueprint director save the information about a blueprint?
<--- Score

200. Are your most profitable lines of business?
<--- Score

201. How do you make an application to have a product listed on the ETL?
<--- Score

202. How do you engage the workforce, in addition to satisfying them?
<--- Score

203. Who is responsible for errors?
<--- Score

204. What is the recommended frequency of auditing?
<--- Score

205. What are the gaps in your knowledge and experience?
<--- Score

206. Do IBM InfoSphere DataStage rules make a reasonable demand on a users capabilities?
<--- Score

207. How do you best change your business model to gain further competitive advantage?
<--- Score

208. Is there a work around that you can use?
<--- Score

209. What is your organization of Commerce Interface?
<--- Score

210. Are new benefits received and understood?
<--- Score

211. Which infosphere information server tools are installed?
<--- Score

212. Are system resources keeping up with requests?
<--- Score

213. How do you foster the skills, knowledge, talents, attributes, and characteristics you want to have?
<--- Score

214. What criteria should project teams use to review and select ETL vendors and tools?
<--- Score

215. What is ETL, what is the practical effect of it here?
<--- Score

216. What can it do to better ensure the high quality delivery of business applications?
<--- Score

217. What are the business rules that are applied

to profit margin?
<--- Score

218. Is your product currently listed on the ETL?
<--- Score

219. What do we do when new problems arise?
<--- Score

220. How many small custom build applications are available?
<--- Score

221. Has implementation been effective in reaching specified objectives so far?
<--- Score

222. Do you have enough freaky customers in your portfolio pushing you to the limit day in and day out?
<--- Score

223. What kind of backup strategies do you perform?
<--- Score

224. How do you know if your product is eligible for the ETL?
<--- Score

225. How do you run more than one Discovery Engine Service on the same host?
<--- Score

226. Are the assumptions believable and achievable?
<--- Score

227. What current ETL tools are being used?
<--- Score

228. What are the various ETL tools in the Market?
<--- Score

229. What is the difference between ETL tool and olap tools?
<--- Score

230. Have new benefits been realized?
<--- Score

231. How do you connect people and systems together easily?
<--- Score

232. Is there an alternative to buying an expensive commercial ETL tool?
<--- Score

233. What is valid, defaulted, or invalid based on the inferred or known classification?
<--- Score

234. What are the Configuration and Management Components?
<--- Score

235. Are ETL jobs being scheduled at the same time?
<--- Score

236. What can be done to ensure the success of ETL projects?
<--- Score

237. How do you perform functional testing under load?

<--- Score

238. Is there any Load testing tool called Rational Site Load tool?

<--- Score

239. What operation was being performed at the time of the error?

<--- Score

240. Operational - will it work?

<--- Score

241. Is there currently a user support Help Desk?

<--- Score

242. How do you configure a Discovery Engine Service to run more than one Discovery Engine at a time?

<--- Score

243. Which collection algorithm should you choose in the Sequential File stage?

<--- Score

Add up total points for this section:
_ _ _ _ _ = Total points for this section

Divided by: _ _ _ _ _ _ (number of statements answered) = _ _ _ _ _ _
Average score for this section

Transfer your score to the IBM

InfoSphere DataStage Index at the
beginning of the Self-Assessment.

IBM InfoSphere DataStage and Managing Projects, Criteria for Project Managers:

1.0 Initiating Process Group: IBM InfoSphere DataStage

1. What business situation is being addressed?

2. Were resources available as planned?

3. Although the IBM InfoSphere DataStage project manager does not directly manage procurement and contracting activities, who does manage procurement and contracting activities in your organization then if not the PM?

4. If action is called for, what form should it take?

5. Have you evaluated the teams performance and asked for feedback?

6. During which stage of Risk planning are modeling techniques used to determine overall effects of risks on IBM InfoSphere DataStage project objectives for high probability, high impact risks?

7. What were things that you did very well and want to do the same again on the next IBM InfoSphere DataStage project?

8. What input will you be required to provide the IBM InfoSphere DataStage project team?

9. Does it make any difference if you am successful?

10. Were decisions made in a timely manner?

11. What do you need to do?

12. What were things that you did well, and could improve, and how?

13. The IBM InfoSphere DataStage project managers have maximum authority in which type of organization?

14. How well did you do?

15. How well did the chosen processes produce the expected results?

16. What are the overarching issues of your organization?

17. Measurable - are the targets measurable?

18. At which cmmi level are software processes documented, standardized, and integrated into a standard to-be practiced process for your organization?

19. How should needs be met?

20. At which stage, in a typical IBM InfoSphere DataStage project do stake holders have maximum influence?

1.1 Project Charter: IBM InfoSphere DataStage

21. Run it as as a startup?

22. Why have you chosen the aim you have set forth?

23. How do you manage integration?

24. Where does all this information come from?

25. How will you know that a change is an improvement?

26. Who will take notes, document decisions?

27. Must Have?

28. What are the assumptions?

29. Where and how does the team fit within your organization structure?

30. Why do you manage integration?

31. How will you learn more about the process or system you are trying to improve?

32. What metrics could you look at?

33. Why is it important?

34. What is the business need?

35. Who is the sponsor?

36. Why executive support?

37. How high should you set your goals?

38. How will you know a change is an improvement?

39. Are you building in-house ?

1.2 Stakeholder Register: IBM InfoSphere DataStage

40. Who wants to talk about Security?

41. Who is managing stakeholder engagement?

42. Is your organization ready for change?

43. What are the major IBM InfoSphere DataStage project milestones requiring communications or providing communications opportunities?

44. How big is the gap?

45. What & Why?

46. Who are the stakeholders?

47. What is the power of the stakeholder?

48. How will reports be created?

49. How should employers make voices heard?

50. What opportunities exist to provide communications?

51. How much influence do they have on the IBM InfoSphere DataStage project?

1.3 Stakeholder Analysis Matrix: IBM InfoSphere DataStage

52. What advantages do your organizations stakeholders have?

53. Economy - home, abroad?

54. What do your organizations stakeholders do better than anyone else?

55. How are the threatened IBM InfoSphere DataStage project targets being used?

56. Is there a reason why you are or are not not using an external rating system?

57. How affected by the problem(s)?

58. Who has control over whom?

59. Processes, systems, it, communications?

60. Are there two or three that rise to the top, and a couple that are sliding to the bottom?

61. Which conditions out of the control of the management are crucial to contribute for the achievement of the development objective?

62. What do people from other organizations see as your strengths?

63. Are you going to weigh the stakeholders?

64. Do recommendations include actions to address any differential distribution of impacts?

65. What can the IBM InfoSphere DataStage projects outcome be used for?

66. Disadvantages of proposition?

67. Cultural, attitudinal, behavioural?

68. What could your organization improve?

69. Own known vulnerabilities?

70. Are the interests in line with the program objectives?

71. What tools would help you communicate?

2.0 Planning Process Group: IBM InfoSphere DataStage

72. To what extent has the intervention strategy been adapted to the areas of intervention in which it is being implemented?

73. How can you tell when you are done?

74. In which IBM InfoSphere DataStage project management process group is the detailed IBM InfoSphere DataStage project budget created?

75. Are you just doing busywork to pass the time?

76. What will you do to minimize the impact should a risk event occur?

77. To what extent and in what ways are the IBM InfoSphere DataStage project contributing to progress towards organizational reform?

78. What good practices or successful experiences or transferable examples have been identified?

79. You did your readings, yes?

80. What input will you be required to provide the IBM InfoSphere DataStage project team?

81. If a risk event occurs, what will you do?

82. When developing the estimates for IBM

InfoSphere DataStage project phases, you choose to add the individual estimates for the activities that comprise each phase. What type of estimation method are you using?

83. When will the IBM InfoSphere DataStage project be done?

84. Why do it IBM InfoSphere DataStage projects fail?

85. Did you read it correctly?

86. What is the critical path for this IBM InfoSphere DataStage project, and what is the duration of the critical path?

87. In what ways can the governance of the IBM InfoSphere DataStage project be improved so that it has greater likelihood of achieving future sustainability?

88. Is the identification of the problems, inequalities and gaps, with respective causes, clear in the IBM InfoSphere DataStage project?

89. What is the NEXT thing to do?

90. If you are late, will anybody notice?

2.1 Project Management Plan: IBM InfoSphere DataStage

91. What goes into your IBM InfoSphere DataStage project Charter?

92. What would you do differently?

93. What is IBM InfoSphere DataStage project scope management?

94. What is risk management?

95. Was the peer (technical) review of the cost estimates duly coordinated with the cost estimate center of expertise and addressed in the review documentation and certification?

96. Is the budget realistic?

97. When is the IBM InfoSphere DataStage project management plan created?

98. Who manages integration?

99. Who is the IBM InfoSphere DataStage project Manager?

100. Is the engineering content at a feasibility level-of-detail, and is it sufficiently complete, to provide an adequate basis for the baseline cost estimate?

101. How well are you able to manage your risk?

102. What went right?

103. Is there anything you would now do differently on your IBM InfoSphere DataStage project based on past experience?

104. What went wrong?

105. Does the selected plan protect privacy?

106. Are there non-structural buyout or relocation recommendations?

107. Do the proposed changes from the IBM InfoSphere DataStage project include any significant risks to safety?

108. What are the training needs?

2.2 Scope Management Plan: IBM InfoSphere DataStage

109. How many changes are you making?

110. Is each item clearly and completely defined?

111. Have stakeholder accountabilities & responsibilities been clearly defined?

112. Are milestone deliverables effectively tracked and compared to IBM InfoSphere DataStage project plan?

113. Are actuals compared against estimates to analyze and correct variances?

114. Are the appropriate IT resources adequate to meet planned commitments?

115. Has your organization readiness assessment been conducted?

116. Pop quiz – which are the same inputs as in scope planning?

117. Are multiple estimation methods being employed?

118. Are calculations and results of analyzes essentially correct?

119. Does all IBM InfoSphere DataStage project

documentation reside in a common repository for easy access?

120. How relevant is this attribute to this IBM InfoSphere DataStage project or audit?

121. Have all involved IBM InfoSphere DataStage project stakeholders and work groups committed to the IBM InfoSphere DataStage project?

122. How do you plan to control Scope Creep?

123. What problem is being solved by delivering this IBM InfoSphere DataStage project?

124. Are post milestone IBM InfoSphere DataStage project reviews (PMPR) conducted with your organization at least once a year?

125. What if you do not have more detailed information on the report?

126. Have reserves been created to address risks?

127. Is pert / critical path or equivalent methodology being used?

128. Are target dates established for each milestone deliverable?

2.3 Requirements Management Plan: IBM InfoSphere DataStage

129. Who will finally present the work or product(s) for acceptance?

130. What are you counting on?

131. Describe the process for rejecting the IBM InfoSphere DataStage project requirements. Who has the authority to reject IBM InfoSphere DataStage project requirements?

132. How detailed should the IBM InfoSphere DataStage project get?

133. When and how will a requirements baseline be established in this IBM InfoSphere DataStage project?

134. Business analysis scope?

135. Do you have an agreed upon process for alerting the IBM InfoSphere DataStage project Manager if a request for change in requirements leads to a product scope change?

136. What performance metrics will be used?

137. Who will approve the requirements (and if multiple approvers, in what order)?

138. Do you know which stakeholders will participate in the requirements effort?

139. Should you include sub-activities?

140. Is there formal agreement on who has authority to approve a change in requirements?

141. Will the contractors involved take full responsibility?

142. Will the IBM InfoSphere DataStage project requirements become approved in writing?

143. How will requirements be managed?

144. The wbs is developed as part of a joint planning session. and how do you know that youhave done this right?

145. Who will perform the analysis?

146. Will you use tracing to help understand the impact of a change in requirements?

147. Who is responsible for monitoring and tracking the IBM InfoSphere DataStage project requirements?

148. Define the help desk model. who will take full responsibility?

2.4 Requirements Documentation: IBM InfoSphere DataStage

149. How do you get the user to tell you what they want?

150. What images does it conjure?

151. How will requirements be documented and who signs off on them?

152. What is the risk associated with the technology?

153. What facilities must be supported by the system?

154. Has requirements gathering uncovered information that would necessitate changes?

155. What are the attributes of a customer?

156. Does the system provide the functions which best support the customers needs?

157. Can the requirement be changed without a large impact on other requirements?

158. Completeness. are all functions required by the customer included?

159. How will the proposed IBM InfoSphere DataStage project help?

160. Where are business rules being captured?

161. Do your constraints stand?

162. What are the acceptance criteria?

163. What is the risk associated with cost and schedule?

164. How do you know when a Requirement is accurate enough?

165. Where do system and software requirements come from, what are sources?

166. Are all functions required by the customer included?

167. Are there legal issues?

168. What will be the integration problems?

2.5 Requirements Traceability Matrix: IBM InfoSphere DataStage

169. Will you use a Requirements Traceability Matrix?

170. Why do you manage scope?

171. What are the chronologies, contingencies, consequences, criteria?

172. What is the WBS?

173. How do you manage scope?

174. Why use a WBS?

175. Do you have a clear understanding of all subcontracts in place?

176. Describe the process for approving requirements so they can be added to the traceability matrix and IBM InfoSphere DataStage project work can be performed. Will the IBM InfoSphere DataStage project requirements become approved in writing?

177. How will it affect the stakeholders personally in career?

178. What percentage of IBM InfoSphere DataStage projects are producing traceability matrices between requirements and other work products?

179. How small is small enough?

180. Is there a requirements traceability process in place?

2.6 Project Scope Statement: IBM InfoSphere DataStage

181. Will the risk documents be filed?

182. Is there a baseline plan against which to measure progress?

183. If there are vendors, have they signed off on the IBM InfoSphere DataStage project Plan?

184. Will all IBM InfoSphere DataStage project issues be unconditionally tracked through the issue resolution process?

185. Have the reports to be produced, distributed, and filed been defined?

186. What is change?

187. Does the scope statement still need some clarity?

188. IBM InfoSphere DataStage project lead, team lead, solution architect?

189. If there is an independent oversight contractor, have they signed off on the IBM InfoSphere DataStage project Plan?

190. Is your organization structure appropriate for the IBM InfoSphere DataStage projects size and complexity?

191. Were potential customers involved early in the planning process?

192. Will the IBM InfoSphere DataStage project risks be managed according to the IBM InfoSphere DataStage projects risk management process?

193. Will the risk plan be updated on a regular and frequent basis?

194. What are the possible consequences should a risk come to occur?

195. Will you need a statement of work?

196. Was planning completed before the IBM InfoSphere DataStage project was initiated?

197. How often will scope changes be reviewed?

198. Is the IBM InfoSphere DataStage project organization documented and on file?

2.7 Assumption and Constraint Log: IBM InfoSphere DataStage

199. Is the process working, and people are not executing in compliance of the process?

200. What threats might prevent you from getting there?

201. Should factors be unpredictable over time?

202. How are new requirements or changes to requirements identified?

203. Are there ways to reduce the time it takes to get something approved?

204. Are formal code reviews conducted?

205. Does the document/deliverable meet general requirements (for example, statement of work) for all deliverables?

206. What weaknesses do you have?

207. Have adequate resources been provided by management to ensure IBM InfoSphere DataStage project success?

208. Is there a Steering Committee in place?

209. Are there unnecessary steps that are creating bottlenecks and/or causing people to wait?

210. What would you gain if you spent time working to improve this process?

211. Model-building: what data-analytic strategies are useful when building proportional-hazards models?

212. Contradictory information between different documents?

213. Does the traceability documentation describe the tool and/or mechanism to be used to capture traceability throughout the life cycle?

214. Are there standards for code development?

215. Can you perform this task or activity in a more effective manner?

216. Have the scope, objectives, costs, benefits and impacts been communicated to all involved and/or impacted stakeholders and work groups?

217. Is the amount of effort justified by the anticipated value of forming a new process?

218. Are processes for release management of new development from coding and unit testing, to integration testing, to training, and production defined and followed?

2.8 Work Breakdown Structure: IBM InfoSphere DataStage

219. How much detail?

220. When do you stop?

221. Why would you develop a Work Breakdown Structure?

222. Who has to do it?

223. What is the probability of completing the IBM InfoSphere DataStage project in less that xx days?

224. When would you develop a Work Breakdown Structure?

225. How will you and your IBM InfoSphere DataStage project team define the IBM InfoSphere DataStage projects scope and work breakdown structure?

226. Do you need another level?

227. How big is a work-package?

228. Can you make it?

229. Is it still viable?

230. How many levels?

231. How far down?

232. Why is it useful?

233. Where does it take place?

234. Is it a change in scope?

2.9 WBS Dictionary: IBM InfoSphere DataStage

235. Is each control account assigned to a single organizational element directly responsible for the work and identifiable to a single element of the CWBS?

236. Are the contractors estimates of costs at completion reconcilable with cost data reported to us?

237. Are the rates for allocating costs from each indirect cost pool to contracts updated as necessary to ensure a realistic monthly allocation of indirect costs without significant year-end adjustments?

238. Are IBM InfoSphere DataStage projected overhead costs in each pool and the associated direct costs used as the basis for establishing interim rates for allocating overhead to contracts?

239. Do procedures specify under what circumstances replanning of open work packages may occur, and the methods to be followed?

240. Does the contractors system provide unit or lot costs when applicable?

241. Cwbs elements to be subcontracted, with identification of subcontractors?

242. Are the overhead pools formally and adequately

identified?

243. Budgeted cost for work performed?

244. Authorization to proceed with all authorized work?

245. Time-phased control account budgets?

246. Does the contractors system include procedures for measuring the performance of critical subcontractors?

247. Changes in the direct base to which overhead costs are allocated?

248. Identify and isolate causes of favorable and unfavorable cost and schedule variances?

249. Are current budgets resulting from changes to the authorized work and/or internal replanning, reconcilable to original budgets for specified reporting items?

250. Are records maintained to show how undistributed budgets are controlled?

251. Are control accounts opened and closed based on the start and completion of work contained therein?

252. Are the requirements for all items of overhead established by rational, traceable processes?

253. Identify potential or actual budget-based and time-based schedule variances?

2.10 Schedule Management Plan: IBM InfoSphere DataStage

254. Are the activity durations realistic and at an appropriate level of detail for effective management?

255. Are vendor invoices audited for accuracy before payment?

256. Is a process defined to measure the performance of the schedule management process itself?

257. Is the ims used by all levels of management for IBM InfoSphere DataStage project implementation and control?

258. Is there general agreement & acceptance of the current status and progress of the IBM InfoSphere DataStage project?

259. Does the ims include all contract and/or designated management control milestones?

260. Is there an approved case?

261. Has a resource management plan been created?

262. Is your organization certified as a broker of the products/supplies?

263. Are estimating assumptions and constraints captured?

264. How are IBM InfoSphere DataStage projects different from operations?

265. Where is the scheduling tool and who has access to it to view it?

266. Does a documented IBM InfoSphere DataStage project organizational policy & plan (i.e. governance model) exist?

267. Does the IBM InfoSphere DataStage project have a Statement of Work?

268. Are internal IBM InfoSphere DataStage project status meetings held at reasonable intervals?

269. Is the plan consistent with industry best practices?

270. Are risk oriented checklists used during risk identification?

271. Are all activities captured and do they address all approved work scope in the IBM InfoSphere DataStage project baseline?

272. Is the development plan and/or process documented?

273. Is it standard practice to formally commit stakeholders to the IBM InfoSphere DataStage project via agreements?

2.11 Activity List: IBM InfoSphere DataStage

274. What will be performed?

275. Where will it be performed?

276. For other activities, how much delay can be tolerated?

277. How will it be performed?

278. What is the LF and LS for each activity?

279. What went well?

280. What is your organizations history in doing similar activities?

281. Is there anything planned that does not need to be here?

282. How should ongoing costs be monitored to try to keep the IBM InfoSphere DataStage project within budget?

283. What is the probability the IBM InfoSphere DataStage project can be completed in xx weeks?

284. How can the IBM InfoSphere DataStage project be displayed graphically to better visualize the activities?

285. Who will perform the work?

286. Are the required resources available or need to be acquired?

287. Can you determine the activity that must finish, before this activity can start?

288. How detailed should a IBM InfoSphere DataStage project get?

289. Is infrastructure setup part of your IBM InfoSphere DataStage project?

290. In what sequence?

2.12 Activity Attributes: IBM InfoSphere DataStage

291. Is there a trend during the year?

292. How do you manage time?

293. How much activity detail is required?

294. Resources to accomplish the work?

295. Activity: what is Missing?

296. Which method produces the more accurate cost assignment?

297. Activity: fair or not fair?

298. Activity: what is In the Bag?

299. Can more resources be added?

300. What is the general pattern here?

301. Would you consider either of corresponding activities an outlier?

302. What is missing?

303. What conclusions/generalizations can you draw from this?

304. Have constraints been applied to the start and

finish milestones for the phases?

305. Where else does it apply?

306. Do you feel very comfortable with your prediction?

2.13 Milestone List: IBM InfoSphere DataStage

307. What are your competitors vulnerabilities?

308. Marketing - reach, distribution, awareness?

309. How late can the activity start?

310. How late can each activity be finished and started?

311. How difficult will it be to do specific activities on this IBM InfoSphere DataStage project?

312. How soon can the activity finish?

313. How late can the activity finish?

314. Describe the industry you are in and the market growth opportunities. What is the market for your technology, product or service?

315. Milestone pages should display the UserID of the person who added the milestone. Does a report or query exist that provides this audit information?

316. Gaps in capabilities?

317. Sustainable financial backing?

318. Level of the Innovation?

319. Global influences?

320. Competitive advantages?

321. Insurmountable weaknesses?

322. Calculate how long can activity be delayed?

323. What would happen if a delivery of material was one week late?

324. How will you get the word out to customers?

325. What specific improvements did you make to the IBM InfoSphere DataStage project proposal since the previous time?

2.14 Network Diagram: IBM InfoSphere DataStage

326. If the IBM InfoSphere DataStage project network diagram cannot change and you have extra personnel resources, what is the BEST thing to do?

327. What must be completed before an activity can be started?

328. What are the Key Success Factors?

329. Where do you schedule uncertainty time?

330. Will crashing x weeks return more in benefits than it costs?

331. What to do and When?

332. What are the tools?

333. Are the gantt chart and/or network diagram updated periodically and used to assess the overall IBM InfoSphere DataStage project timetable?

334. How confident can you be in your milestone dates and the delivery date?

335. How difficult will it be to do specific activities on this IBM InfoSphere DataStage project?

336. Exercise: what is the probability that the IBM InfoSphere DataStage project duration will exceed xx

weeks?

337. If a current contract exists, can you provide the vendor name, contract start, and contract expiration date?

338. If x is long, what would be the completion time if you break x into two parallel parts of y weeks and z weeks?

339. Planning: who, how long, what to do?

340. What job or jobs follow it?

341. Why must you schedule milestones, such as reviews, throughout the IBM InfoSphere DataStage project?

342. What job or jobs could run concurrently?

343. What activities must occur simultaneously with this activity?

2.15 Activity Resource Requirements: IBM InfoSphere DataStage

344. Do you use tools like decomposition and rolling-wave planning to produce the activity list and other outputs?

345. Time for overtime?

346. Other support in specific areas?

347. Why do you do that?

348. Organizational Applicability?

349. How do you handle petty cash?

350. Are there unresolved issues that need to be addressed?

351. Which logical relationship does the PDM use most often?

352. When does monitoring begin?

353. What is the Work Plan Standard?

354. How many signatures do you require on a check and does this match what is in your policy and procedures?

355. Anything else?

356. What are constraints that you might find during the Human Resource Planning process?

2.16 Resource Breakdown Structure: IBM InfoSphere DataStage

357. Which resources should be in the resource pool?

358. Why time management?

359. What is the difference between % Complete and % work?

360. Is predictive resource analysis being done?

361. What is each stakeholders desired outcome for the IBM InfoSphere DataStage project?

362. The list could probably go on, but, the thing that you would most like to know is, How long & How much?

363. How can this help you with team building?

364. How should the information be delivered?

365. Who is allowed to see what data about which resources?

366. Goals for the IBM InfoSphere DataStage project. What is each stakeholders desired outcome for the IBM InfoSphere DataStage project?

367. Why is this important?

368. What is the primary purpose of the human

resource plan?

369. Are the required resources available?

370. What are the requirements for resource data?

371. Changes based on input from stakeholders?

372. What defines a successful IBM InfoSphere DataStage project?

373. What is IBM InfoSphere DataStage project communication management?

374. What defines a successful IBM InfoSphere DataStage project?

2.17 Activity Duration Estimates: IBM InfoSphere DataStage

375. Are measurement techniques employed to determine the potential impact of proposed changes?

376. What is involved in the solicitation process?

377. Are team building activities completed to improve team performance?

378. What are the main parts of a scope statement?

379. What are the main types of goods and services being outsourced?

380. Will it help in finding or retaining employees?

381. (Cpi), and schedule performance index (spi) for the IBM InfoSphere DataStage project?

382. Does a process exist to determine the potential loss or gain if risk events occur?

383. Is a work breakdown structure created to organize and to confirm the scope of each IBM InfoSphere DataStage project?

384. What is the BEST thing to do?

385. What are the typical challenges IBM InfoSphere DataStage project teams face during each of the five process groups?

386. What is the difference between using brainstorming and the Delphi technique for risk identification?

387. Does a process exist to determine which risk events to accept and which events to disregard?

388. Account for the four frames of organizations. How can they help IBM InfoSphere DataStage project managers understand your organizational context for IBM InfoSphere DataStage projects?

389. Is the IBM InfoSphere DataStage project performing better or worse than planned?

390. Are IBM InfoSphere DataStage project costs tracked in the general ledger?

391. How have experts such as Deming, Juran, Crosby, and Taguchi affected the quality movement and todays use of Six Sigma?

392. Which best describes the relationship between standard deviation and risk?

393. Why is activity definition the first process involved in IBM InfoSphere DataStage project time management?

394. Is risk identification completed regularly throughout the IBM InfoSphere DataStage project?

2.18 Duration Estimating Worksheet: IBM InfoSphere DataStage

395. Does the IBM InfoSphere DataStage project provide innovative ways for stakeholders to overcome obstacles or deliver better outcomes?

396. Done before proceeding with this activity or what can be done concurrently?

397. Is the IBM InfoSphere DataStage project responsive to community need?

398. Is this operation cost effective?

399. When, then?

400. Can the IBM InfoSphere DataStage project be constructed as planned?

401. What is your role?

402. What is the total time required to complete the IBM InfoSphere DataStage project if no delays occur?

403. How should ongoing costs be monitored to try to keep the IBM InfoSphere DataStage project within budget?

404. Why estimate time and cost?

405. Is a construction detail attached (to aid in explanation)?

406. When does your organization expect to be able to complete it?

407. Define the work as completely as possible. What work will be included in the IBM InfoSphere DataStage project?

408. What is cost and IBM InfoSphere DataStage project cost management?

409. Why estimate costs?

410. When do the individual activities need to start and finish?

411. Small or large IBM InfoSphere DataStage project?

412. Science = process: remember the scientific method?

413. Value pocket identification & quantification what are value pockets?

414. What is next?

2.19 Project Schedule: IBM InfoSphere DataStage

415. How do you know that youhave done this right?

416. If there are any qualifying green components to this IBM InfoSphere DataStage project, what portion of the total IBM InfoSphere DataStage project cost is green?

417. What documents, if any, will the subcontractor provide (eg IBM InfoSphere DataStage project schedule, quality plan etc)?

418. Activity charts and bar charts are graphical representations of a IBM InfoSphere DataStage project schedule ...how do they differ?

419. Why is software IBM InfoSphere DataStage project disaster so common?

420. How closely did the initial IBM InfoSphere DataStage project Schedule compare with the actual schedule?

421. What is risk?

422. Why do you need schedules?

423. Is the IBM InfoSphere DataStage project schedule available for all IBM InfoSphere DataStage project team members to review?

424. Are quality inspections and review activities listed in the IBM InfoSphere DataStage project schedule(s)?

425. IBM InfoSphere DataStage project work estimates Who is managing the work estimate quality of work tasks in the IBM InfoSphere DataStage project schedule?

426. Are procedures defined by which the IBM InfoSphere DataStage project schedule may be changed?

427. Why is this particularly bad?

428. How do you manage IBM InfoSphere DataStage project Risk?

429. Are there activities that came from a template or previous IBM InfoSphere DataStage project that are not applicable on this phase of this IBM InfoSphere DataStage project?

430. Why do you think schedule issues often cause the most conflicts on IBM InfoSphere DataStage projects?

431. Verify that the update is accurate. Are all remaining durations correct?

2.20 Cost Management Plan: IBM InfoSphere DataStage

432. Does the business case include how the IBM InfoSphere DataStage project aligns with your organizations strategic goals & objectives?

433. Are internal IBM InfoSphere DataStage project status meetings held at reasonable intervals?

434. Is a pmo (IBM InfoSphere DataStage project management office) in place and provide oversight to the IBM InfoSphere DataStage project?

435. Alignment to strategic goals & objectives?

436. Have the reasons why the changes to your organizational systems and capabilities are required?

437. Is the schedule updated on a periodic basis?

438. Are changes in scope (deliverable commitments) agreed to by all affected groups & individuals?

439. Are the schedule estimates reasonable given the IBM InfoSphere DataStage project?

440. Are meeting minutes captured and sent out after the meeting?

441. What is cost and IBM InfoSphere DataStage project cost management?

442. Has the budget been baselined?

443. Does a documented IBM InfoSphere DataStage project organizational policy & plan (i.e. governance model) exist?

444. What are the IBM InfoSphere DataStage project objectives?

445. Are vendor contract reports, reviews and visits conducted periodically?

446. Were IBM InfoSphere DataStage project team members involved in the development of activity & task decomposition?

447. Are IBM InfoSphere DataStage project leaders committed to this IBM InfoSphere DataStage project full time?

448. Is there a formal set of procedures supporting Stakeholder Management?

449. Milestones – what are the key dates in executing the contract plan?

450. Are written status reports provided on a designated frequent basis?

451. Are any non-compliance issues that exist due to State practices communicated to your organization?

2.21 Activity Cost Estimates: IBM InfoSphere DataStage

452. The impact and what actions were taken?

453. Can you delete activities or make them inactive?

454. Will you need to provide essential services information about activities?

455. How many activities should you have?

456. Does the activity rely on a common set of tools to carry it out?

457. Where can you get activity reports?

458. Which contract type places the most risk on the seller?

459. How do you allocate indirect costs to activities?

460. What makes a good expected result statement?

461. What are you looking for?

462. Based on your IBM InfoSphere DataStage project communication management plan, what worked well?

463. Were you satisfied with the work?

464. Will you use any tools, such as IBM InfoSphere

DataStage project management software, to assist in capturing Earned Value metrics?

465. How do you change activities?

466. What communication items need improvement?

467. What is the activity recast of the budget?

468. Is there anything unique in this IBM InfoSphere DataStage projects scope statement that will affect resources?

469. What defines a successful IBM InfoSphere DataStage project?

2.22 Cost Estimating Worksheet: IBM InfoSphere DataStage

470. Identify the timeframe necessary to monitor progress and collect data to determine how the selected measure has changed?

471. How will the results be shared and to whom?

472. What can be included?

473. Can a trend be established from historical performance data on the selected measure and are the criteria for using trend analysis or forecasting methods met?

474. Is it feasible to establish a control group arrangement?

475. What is the estimated labor cost today based upon this information?

476. What info is needed?

477. What is the purpose of estimating?

478. What additional IBM InfoSphere DataStage project(s) could be initiated as a result of this IBM InfoSphere DataStage project?

479. Does the IBM InfoSphere DataStage project provide innovative ways for stakeholders to overcome obstacles or deliver better outcomes?

480. Is the IBM InfoSphere DataStage project responsive to community need?

481. What happens to any remaining funds not used?

482. What will others want?

483. Ask: are others positioned to know, are others credible, and will others cooperate?

484. What costs are to be estimated?

485. Who is best positioned to know and assist in identifying corresponding factors?

486. Will the IBM InfoSphere DataStage project collaborate with the local community and leverage resources?

2.23 Cost Baseline: IBM InfoSphere DataStage

487. How fast?

488. Has the IBM InfoSphere DataStage project documentation been archived or otherwise disposed as described in the IBM InfoSphere DataStage project communication plan?

489. Have the resources used by the IBM InfoSphere DataStage project been reassigned to other units or IBM InfoSphere DataStage projects?

490. Has the IBM InfoSphere DataStage project (or IBM InfoSphere DataStage project phase) been evaluated against each objective established in the product description and Integrated IBM InfoSphere DataStage project Plan?

491. IBM InfoSphere DataStage project goals -should others be reconsidered?

492. Vac -variance at completion, how much over/ under budget do you expect to be?

493. On budget?

494. Does the suggested change request seem to represent a necessary enhancement to the product?

495. Have the actual milestone completion dates been compared to the approved schedule?

496. What deliverables come first?

497. At which frequency ?

498. How do you manage cost?

499. What do you want to measure ?

500. Has the documentation relating to operation and maintenance of the product(s) or service(s) been delivered to, and accepted by, operations management?

501. What is cost and IBM InfoSphere DataStage project cost management?

502. Eac -estimate at completion, what is the total job expected to cost?

503. How long are you willing to wait before you find out were late?

504. Does a process exist for establishing a cost baseline to measure IBM InfoSphere DataStage project performance?

2.24 Quality Management Plan: IBM InfoSphere DataStage

505. Results Available?

506. Has a IBM InfoSphere DataStage project Communications Plan been developed?

507. How does training support what is important to your organization and the individual?

508. Are there processes in place to ensure internal consistency between the source code components?

509. What field records are generated?

510. Does the IBM InfoSphere DataStage project have a formal IBM InfoSphere DataStage project Plan?

511. What is the Quality Management Plan?

512. Why quality management?

513. How does your organization perform analyzes to assess overall organizational performance and set priorities?

514. Are there trends or hot spots?

515. When reporting to different audiences, do you vary the form or type of report?

516. Methodology followed?

517. Account for the procedures used to verify the data quality of the data being reviewed?

518. Have all necessary approvals been obtained?

519. Are requirements management tracking tools and procedures in place?

520. How are corresponding standards measured?

521. What are your organizations current levels and trends for the already stated measures related to customer satisfaction/ dissatisfaction and product/ service performance?

522. What are the appropriate test methods to be used?

2.25 Quality Metrics: IBM InfoSphere DataStage

523. Are quality metrics defined?

524. How are requirements conflicts resolved?

525. Is material complete (and does it meet the standards)?

526. Do you know how much profit a 10% decrease in waste would generate?

527. What is the timeline to meet your goal?

528. Product Availability ?

529. What is the benchmark?

530. Do you stratify metrics by product or site?

531. What about still open problems?

532. Filter visualizations of interest?

533. What percentage are outcome-based?

534. Are interface issues coordinated?

535. Are applicable standards referenced and available?

536. How does one achieve stability?

537. Which report did you use to create the data you are submitting?

538. How exactly do you define when differences exist?

539. Where is quality now?

540. What level of statistical confidence do you use?

541. Was review conducted per standard protocols?

2.26 Process Improvement Plan: IBM InfoSphere DataStage

542. Have the frequency of collection and the points in the process where measurements will be made been determined?

543. What lessons have you learned so far?

544. Who should prepare the process improvement action plan?

545. Are you making progress on the goals?

546. Where are you now?

547. Where do you want to be?

548. Does explicit definition of the measures exist?

549. Management commitment at all levels?

550. What personnel are the sponsors for that initiative?

551. Has the time line required to move measurement results from the points of collection to databases or users been established?

552. Modeling current processes is great, and will you ever see a return on that investment?

553. What actions are needed to address the

problems and achieve the goals?

554. Why do you want to achieve the goal?

555. If a process improvement framework is being used, which elements will help the problems and goals listed?

556. What is the test-cycle concept?

557. How do you manage quality?

558. Have the supporting tools been developed or acquired?

559. What personnel are the champions for the initiative?

560. What is quality and how will you ensure it?

2.27 Responsibility Assignment Matrix: IBM InfoSphere DataStage

561. Does each activity-deliverable have exactly one Accountable responsibility, so that accountability is clear and decisions can be made quickly?

562. No rs: if a task has no one listed as responsible, who is getting the job done?

563. Are detailed work packages planned as far in advance as practicable?

564. What is the number one predictor of a groups productivity?

565. Too many is: do all the identified roles need to be routinely informed or only in exceptional circumstances?

566. What are the deliverables?

567. If a role has only Signing-off, or only Communicating responsibility and has no Performing, Accountable, or Monitoring responsibility, is it necessary?

568. Direct labor dollars and/or hours?

569. Changes in the current direct and IBM InfoSphere DataStage projected base?

570. Will too many Communicating responsibilities

tangle the IBM InfoSphere DataStage project in unnecessary communications?

571. Changes in the nature of the overhead requirements?

572. Contemplated overhead expenditure for each period based on the best information currently available?

573. Is work progressively subdivided into detailed work packages as requirements are defined?

574. Most people let you know when others re too busy, and are others really too busy?

575. Are material costs reported within the same period as that in which BCWP is earned for that material?

576. How do you manage remotely to staff in other Divisions?

577. Past experience – the person or the group worked at something similar in the past?

2.28 Roles and Responsibilities: IBM InfoSphere DataStage

578. Are IBM InfoSphere DataStage project team roles and responsibilities identified and documented?

579. Who: who is involved?

580. Is there a training program in place for stakeholders covering expectations, roles and responsibilities and any addition knowledge others need to be good stakeholders?

581. Are the quality assurance functions and related roles and responsibilities clearly defined?

582. What areas of supervision are challenging for you?

583. Concern: where are you limited or have no authority, where you can not influence?

584. Be specific; avoid generalities. Thank you and great work alone are insufficient. What exactly do you appreciate and why?

585. Have you ever been a part of this team?

586. Is feedback clearly communicated and non-judgmental?

587. Are your policies supportive of a culture of quality data?

588. What is working well within your organizations performance management system?

589. What expectations were NOT met?

590. Is the data complete?

591. To decide whether to use a quality measurement, ask how will you know when it is achieved?

592. Are governance roles and responsibilities documented?

593. Are your budgets supportive of a culture of quality data?

594. Once the responsibilities are defined for the IBM InfoSphere DataStage project, have the deliverables, roles and responsibilities been clearly communicated to every participant?

595. What expectations were met?

596. Who is responsible for implementation activities and where will the functions, roles and responsibilities be defined?

597. Who is responsible for each task?

2.29 Human Resource Management Plan: IBM InfoSphere DataStage

598. Has the scope management document been updated and distributed to help prevent scope creep?

599. Have all involved IBM InfoSphere DataStage project stakeholders and work groups committed to the IBM InfoSphere DataStage project?

600. Is the steering committee active in IBM InfoSphere DataStage project oversight?

601. Quality assurance overheads?

602. Are tasks tracked by hours?

603. Pareto diagrams, statistical sampling, flow charting or trend analysis used quality monitoring?

604. Sensitivity analysis?

605. Are risk triggers captured?

606. What areas does the group agree are the biggest success on the IBM InfoSphere DataStage project?

607. Is the current culture aligned with the vision, mission, and values of the department?

608. Are post milestone IBM InfoSphere DataStage project reviews (PMPR) conducted with your organization at least once a year?

609. Is quality monitored from the perspective of the customers needs and expectations?

610. Does the schedule include IBM InfoSphere DataStage project management time and change request analysis time?

611. Have activity relationships and interdependencies within tasks been adequately identified?

612. Does the detailed work plan match the complexity of tasks with the capabilities of personnel?

613. Does the IBM InfoSphere DataStage project have a Statement of Work?

2.30 Communications Management Plan: IBM InfoSphere DataStage

614. Who did you turn to if you had questions?

615. Who is involved as you identify stakeholders?

616. Do you prepare stakeholder engagement plans?

617. Who to learn from?

618. Who is the stakeholder?

619. Timing: when do the effects of the communication take place?

620. Do you feel a register helps?

621. What approaches do you use?

622. How will the person responsible for executing the communication item be notified?

623. Are others needed?

624. Do you ask; can you recommend others for you to talk with about this initiative?

625. Is the stakeholder role recognized by your organization?

626. What to know?

627. Who will use or be affected by the result of a IBM InfoSphere DataStage project?

628. What approaches to you feel are the best ones to use?

629. How is this initiative related to other portfolios, programs, or IBM InfoSphere DataStage projects?

630. Which team member will work with each stakeholder?

631. Are you constantly rushing from meeting to meeting?

632. Why is stakeholder engagement important?

633. Who needs to know and how much?

2.31 Risk Management Plan: IBM InfoSphere DataStage

634. Was an original risk assessment/risk management plan completed?

635. Are requirements fully understood by the software engineering team and customers?

636. What can go wrong?

637. What are the cost, schedule and resource impacts of avoiding the risk?

638. What are the chances the event will occur?

639. How much risk can you tolerate?

640. Are tool mentors available?

641. What is the cost to the IBM InfoSphere DataStage project if it does occur?

642. Risk probability and impact: how will the probabilities and impacts of risk items be assessed?

643. Management -what contingency plans do you have if the risk becomes a reality?

644. Do end-users have realistic expectations?

645. Are some people working on multiple IBM InfoSphere DataStage projects?

646. Is security a central objective?

647. Are certain activities taking a long time to complete?

648. Could others have been better mitigated?

649. Do requirements put excessive performance constraints on the product?

650. Can the IBM InfoSphere DataStage project proceed without assuming the risk?

651. Risks should be identified during which phase of IBM InfoSphere DataStage project management life cycle?

652. What is the impact to the IBM InfoSphere DataStage project if the item is not resolved in a timely fashion?

653. Are you working on the right risks?

2.32 Risk Register: IBM InfoSphere DataStage

654. Market risk -will the new service or product be useful to your organization or marketable to others?

655. What are you going to do to limit the IBM InfoSphere DataStage projects risk exposure due to the identified risks?

656. Technology risk -is the IBM InfoSphere DataStage project technically feasible?

657. Who needs to know about this?

658. Assume the event happens, what is the Most Likely impact?

659. How well are risks controlled?

660. Who is accountable?

661. Are implemented controls working as others should?

662. People risk -are people with appropriate skills available to help complete the IBM InfoSphere DataStage project?

663. Preventative actions - planned actions to reduce the likelihood a risk will occur and/or reduce the seriousness should it occur. What should you do now?

664. What risks might negatively or positively affect achieving the IBM InfoSphere DataStage project objectives?

665. Risk categories: what are the main categories of risks that should be addressed on this IBM InfoSphere DataStage project?

666. What are the main aims, objectives of the policy, strategy, or service and the intended outcomes?

667. What may happen or not go according to plan?

668. Recovery actions - planned actions taken once a risk has occurred to allow you to move on. What should you do after?

669. What should the audit role be in establishing a risk management process?

670. Which key risks have ineffective responses or outstanding improvement actions?

671. What would the impact to the IBM InfoSphere DataStage project objectives be should the risk arise?

2.33 Probability and Impact Assessment: IBM InfoSphere DataStage

672. Who should be notified of the occurrence of each of the risk indicators?

673. Are the facilities, expertise, resources, and management know-how available to handle the situation?

674. Are there any IBM InfoSphere DataStage projects similar to this one in existence?

675. Which functions, departments, and activities of your organization are going to be affected?

676. What are its business ethics?

677. What is the likelihood of a breakthrough?

678. Risk categorization -which of your categories has more risk than others?

679. What should be the external organizations responsibility vis-à-vis total stake in the IBM InfoSphere DataStage project?

680. Sensitivity analysis -which risks will have the most impact on the IBM InfoSphere DataStage project?

681. Do you use diagramming techniques to show

cause and effect?

682. Who will be responsible for a slippage?

683. How are the local factors going to affect the absorption?

684. Have customers been involved fully in the definition of requirements?

685. How do the products attain the specifications?

686. Which role do you have in the IBM InfoSphere DataStage project?

687. Will new information become available during the IBM InfoSphere DataStage project?

688. Risk data quality assessment - what is the quality of the data used to determine or assess the risk?

689. How is risk handled within this IBM InfoSphere DataStage project organization?

690. What are the channels available for distribution to the customer?

2.34 Probability and Impact Matrix: IBM InfoSphere DataStage

691. Is IBM InfoSphere DataStage project scope stable?

692. Is the process supported by tools?

693. Are the risk data complete?

694. What is the risk appetite?

695. Can you stabilize dynamic risk factors?

696. What are the likely future requirements?

697. Is the technology to be built new to your organization?

698. Mandated delivery date?

699. What risks are necessary to achieve success?

700. Have staff received necessary training?

701. What changes in the regulation are forthcoming?

702. How completely has the customer been identified?

703. Can the risk be avoided by choosing a different alternative?

704. What is IBM InfoSphere DataStage project risk management?

705. Do you have a mechanism for managing change?

706. Are flexibility and reuse paramount?

707. What has the IBM InfoSphere DataStage project manager forgotten to do?

2.35 Risk Data Sheet: IBM InfoSphere DataStage

708. What are your core values?

709. Risk of what?

710. Has a sensitivity analysis been carried out?

711. What if client refuses?

712. What are you trying to achieve (Objectives)?

713. How do you handle product safely?

714. Whom do you serve (customers)?

715. Are new hazards created?

716. During work activities could hazards exist?

717. What is the chance that it will happen?

718. What are you weak at and therefore need to do better?

719. What are the main threats to your existence?

720. What were the Causes that contributed?

721. Potential for recurrence?

722. What can happen?

723. How can hazards be reduced?

724. What is the environment within which you operate (social trends, economic, community values, broad based participation, national directions etc.)?

725. How can it happen?

2.36 Procurement Management Plan: IBM InfoSphere DataStage

726. Does the IBM InfoSphere DataStage project have a Statement of Work?

727. Was your organizations estimating methodology being used and followed?

728. Do you have the reasons why the changes to your organizational systems and capabilities are required?

729. Have adequate resources been provided by management to ensure IBM InfoSphere DataStage project success?

730. Is the communication plan being followed?

731. What is a IBM InfoSphere DataStage project Management Plan?

732. Is there a procurement management plan in place?

733. Does all IBM InfoSphere DataStage project documentation reside in a common repository for easy access?

734. Are the payment terms being followed?

735. Have all documents been archived in a IBM InfoSphere DataStage project repository for each

release?

736. How and when do you enter into IBM InfoSphere DataStage project Procurement Management?

737. Financial capacity; does the seller have, or can the seller reasonably be expected to obtain, the financial resources needed?

738. What types of contracts will be used?

739. Are the IBM InfoSphere DataStage project plans updated on a frequent basis?

740. Does the resource management plan include a personnel development plan?

741. Are trade-offs between accepting the risk and mitigating the risk identified?

742. Were escalated issues resolved promptly?

2.37 Source Selection Criteria: IBM InfoSphere DataStage

743. Are types/quantities of material, facilities appropriate?

744. What common questions or problems are associated with debriefings?

745. How do you manage procurement?

746. Who is entitled to a debriefing?

747. How do you consolidate reviews and analysis of evaluators?

748. How are clarifications and communications appropriately used?

749. What does an evaluation address and what does a sample resemble?

750. What information may not be provided?

751. What source selection software is your team using?

752. What can not be disclosed?

753. Does your documentation identify why the team concurs or differs with reported performance from past performance report (CPARs, questionnaire responses, etc.)?

754. Are there any specific considerations that precludes offers from being selected as the awardee?

755. What is price analysis and when should it be performed?

756. What instructions should be provided regarding oral presentations?

757. What are the steps in performing a cost/tech tradeoff?

758. With the rapid changes in information technology, will media be readable in five or ten years?

759. What is the last item a IBM InfoSphere DataStage project manager must do to finalize IBM InfoSphere DataStage project close-out?

760. What benefits are accrued from issuing a DRFP in advance of issuing a final RFP?

761. What are the limitations on pre-competitive range communications?

762. What does a sample rating scale look like?

2.38 Stakeholder Management Plan: IBM InfoSphere DataStage

763. What are the criteria for selecting other suppliers, including subcontractors?

764. Does the IBM InfoSphere DataStage project have a formal IBM InfoSphere DataStage project Charter?

765. Has a sponsor been identified?

766. Is the current scope of the IBM InfoSphere DataStage project substantially different than that originally defined?

767. Are non-critical path items updated and agreed upon with the teams?

768. What is the drawback in using qualitative IBM InfoSphere DataStage project selection techniques?

769. Has the business need been clearly defined?

770. Are corrective actions and variances reported?

771. Where are the verification requirements to be documented (eg purchase order, agreement etc)?

772. Who might be involved in developing a charter?

773. Will all outputs delivered by the IBM InfoSphere DataStage project follow the same process?

774. Where does the information come from?

775. Have key stakeholders been identified?

776. What records are required (eg purchase orders, agreements)?

777. Is stakeholder involvement adequate?

2.39 Change Management Plan: IBM InfoSphere DataStage

778. Have the systems been configured and tested?

779. Does this change represent a completely new process for your organization, or a different application of an existing process?

780. Is there a support model for this application and are the details available for distribution?

781. What is the most cynical response it can receive?

782. How might they respond to the message and if the response may be negative or open to misinterpretation, what else needs to be said?

783. How frequently should you repeat the message?

784. What communication network would you use – informal or formal?

785. What are the major changes to processes?

786. What goal(s) do you hope to accomplish?

787. What is the worst thing that can happen if you chose not to communicate this information?

788. Has a training need analysis been carried out?

789. How badly can information be misinterpreted?

790. Identify the current level of skills and knowledge and behaviours of the group that will be impacted on. What prerequisite knowledge do corresponding groups need?

791. Do you need new systems?

792. Has the training provider been established?

793. What are the training strategies?

794. How can you best frame the message so that it addresses the audiences interests?

795. Who might present the most resistance?

796. What is the most positive interpretation it can receive?

797. What type of materials/channels will be available to leverage?

3.0 Executing Process Group: IBM InfoSphere DataStage

798. On which process should team members spend the most time?

799. What are the key components of the IBM InfoSphere DataStage project communications plan?

800. Contingency planning. if a risk event occurs, what will you do?

801. It under budget or over budget?

802. Will outside resources be needed to help?

803. Does software appear easy to learn?

804. In what way has the program come up with innovative measures for problem-solving?

805. When do you share the scorecard with managers?

806. Would you rate yourself as being risk-averse, risk-neutral, or risk-seeking?

807. Specific - is the objective clear in terms of what, how, when, and where the situation will be changed?

808. What are the main processes included in IBM InfoSphere DataStage project quality management?

809. Were sponsors and decision makers available when needed outside regularly scheduled meetings?

810. How could stakeholders negatively impact your IBM InfoSphere DataStage project?

811. What does it mean to take a systems view of a IBM InfoSphere DataStage project?

812. Will new hardware or software be required for servers or client machines?

813. How can software assist in IBM InfoSphere DataStage project communications?

814. What is the product of your IBM InfoSphere DataStage project?

3.1 Team Member Status Report: IBM InfoSphere DataStage

815. Are the products of your organizations IBM InfoSphere DataStage projects meeting customers objectives?

816. The problem with Reward & Recognition Programs is that the truly deserving people all too often get left out. How can you make it practical?

817. Is there evidence that staff is taking a more professional approach toward management of your organizations IBM InfoSphere DataStage projects?

818. Will the staff do training or is that done by a third party?

819. How does this product, good, or service meet the needs of the IBM InfoSphere DataStage project and your organization as a whole?

820. How can you make it practical?

821. Are the attitudes of staff regarding IBM InfoSphere DataStage project work improving?

822. Does every department have to have a IBM InfoSphere DataStage project Manager on staff?

823. Are your organizations IBM InfoSphere DataStage projects more successful over time?

824. What specific interest groups do you have in place?

825. How it is to be done?

826. When a teams productivity and success depend on collaboration and the efficient flow of information, what generally fails them?

827. Why is it to be done?

828. Does the product, good, or service already exist within your organization?

829. Does your organization have the means (staff, money, contract, etc.) to produce or to acquire the product, good, or service?

830. How will resource planning be done?

831. How much risk is involved?

832. Do you have an Enterprise IBM InfoSphere DataStage project Management Office (EPMO)?

833. What is to be done?

3.2 Change Request: IBM InfoSphere DataStage

834. Who can suggest changes?

835. Does the schedule include IBM InfoSphere DataStage project management time and change request analysis time?

836. Will all change requests be unconditionally tracked through this process?

837. What should be regulated in a change control operating instruction?

838. Are you implementing itil processes?

839. Who is responsible for the implementation and monitoring of all measures?

840. Who is included in the change control team?

841. How are the measures for carrying out the change established?

842. Are change requests logged and managed?

843. What are the Impacts to your organization?

844. Can static requirements change attributes like the size of the change be used to predict reliability in execution?

845. Where do changes come from?

846. Why were your requested changes rejected or not made?

847. Who is communicating the change?

848. What mechanism is used to appraise others of changes that are made?

849. When do you create a change request?

850. How are changes requested (forms, method of communication)?

851. Will this change conflict with other requirements changes (e.g., lead to conflicting operational scenarios)?

852. What has an inspector to inspect and to check?

3.3 Change Log: IBM InfoSphere DataStage

853. Will the IBM InfoSphere DataStage project fail if the change request is not executed?

854. Is the submitted change a new change or a modification of a previously approved change?

855. When was the request approved?

856. How does this change affect scope?

857. Does the suggested change request represent a desired enhancement to the products functionality?

858. Do the described changes impact on the integrity or security of the system?

859. Is this a mandatory replacement?

860. Who initiated the change request?

861. Is the change request within IBM InfoSphere DataStage project scope?

862. When was the request submitted?

863. How does this change affect the timeline of the schedule?

864. Is the change request open, closed or pending?

865. Should a more thorough impact analysis be conducted?

866. How does this relate to the standards developed for specific business processes?

867. Is the requested change request a result of changes in other IBM InfoSphere DataStage project(s)?

868. Is the change backward compatible without limitations?

3.4 Decision Log: IBM InfoSphere DataStage

869. How effective is maintaining the log at facilitating organizational learning?

870. Meeting purpose; why does this team meet?

871. What makes you different or better than others companies selling the same thing?

872. How do you define success?

873. What is the line where eDiscovery ends and document review begins?

874. Behaviors; what are guidelines that the team has identified that will assist them with getting the most out of team meetings?

875. How does provision of information, both in terms of content and presentation, influence acceptance of alternative strategies?

876. What are the cost implications?

877. How does an increasing emphasis on cost containment influence the strategies and tactics used?

878. What eDiscovery problem or issue did your organization set out to fix or make better?

879. How does the use a Decision Support System influence the strategies/tactics or costs?

880. With whom was the decision shared or considered?

881. What is the average size of your matters in an applicable measurement?

882. Which variables make a critical difference?

883. What alternatives/risks were considered?

884. Who is the decisionmaker?

885. What was the rationale for the decision?

886. Is everything working as expected?

887. Adversarial environment. is your opponent open to a non-traditional workflow, or will it likely challenge anything you do?

888. Linked to original objective?

3.5 Quality Audit: IBM InfoSphere DataStage

889. What is your organizations greatest strength?

890. Are all areas associated with the storage and reconditioning of devices clean, free of rubbish, adequately ventilated and in good repair?

891. What does an analysis of your organizations staff profile suggest in terms of its planning, and how is this being addressed?

892. How does your organization know that its system for governing staff behaviour is appropriately effective and constructive?

893. How does your organization know that its quality of teaching is appropriately effective and constructive?

894. How does your organization know that its staffing profile is optimally aligned with the capability requirements implicit (or explicit) in its Strategic Plan?

895. Does the report read coherently?

896. How does your organization know that its teaching activities (and staff learning) are effectively and constructively enhanced by its activities?

897. Does the suppliers quality system have a written procedure for corrective action when a defect occurs?

898. Why are you trying to do it?

899. How does your organization know that its risk management system is appropriately effective and constructive?

900. Do the suppliers use a formal quality system?

901. Are all records associated with the reconditioning of a device maintained for a minimum of two years after the sale or disposal of the last device within a lot of merchandise?

902. Will the evidence likely be sufficient and appropriate?

903. Is there any content that may be legally actionable?

904. How does your organization know that its system for staff performance planning and review is appropriately effective and constructive?

905. How does your organization know that its staff embody the core knowledge, skills and characteristics for which it wishes to be recognized?

906. Are people allowed to contribute ideas?

907. Have the risks associated with the intentions been identified, analyzed and appropriate responses developed?

3.6 Team Directory: IBM InfoSphere DataStage

908. Process decisions: are all start-up, turn over and close out requirements of the contract satisfied?

909. Do purchase specifications and configurations match requirements?

910. Decisions: is the most suitable form of contract being used?

911. Days from the time the issue is identified?

912. Where should the information be distributed?

913. Does a IBM InfoSphere DataStage project team directory list all resources assigned to the IBM InfoSphere DataStage project?

914. Decisions: what could be done better to improve the quality of the constructed product?

915. How and in what format should information be presented?

916. Who will talk to the customer?

917. Who are your stakeholders (customers, sponsors, end users, team members)?

918. Who are the Team Members?

919. Where will the product be used and/or delivered or built when appropriate?

920. Is construction on schedule?

921. What are you going to deliver or accomplish?

922. Timing: when do the effects of communication take place?

923. Process decisions: do job conditions warrant additional actions to collect job information and document on-site activity?

924. Process decisions: is work progressing on schedule and per contract requirements?

925. Process decisions: how well was task order work performed?

3.7 Team Operating Agreement: IBM InfoSphere DataStage

926. Do you post meeting notes and the recording (if used) and notify participants?

927. Seconds for members to respond?

928. What is a Virtual Team?

929. How will your group handle planned absences?

930. Do you ask participants to close laptops and place mobile devices on silent on the table while the meeting is in progress?

931. Are there differences in access to communication and collaboration technology based on team member location?

932. What are the safety issues/risks that need to be addressed and/or that the team needs to consider?

933. Do you vary your voice pace, tone and pitch to engage participants and gain involvement?

934. Has the appropriate access to relevant data and analysis capability been granted?

935. Are team roles clearly defined and accepted?

936. Are leadership responsibilities shared among team members (versus a single leader)?

937. Do you brief absent members after they view meeting notes or listen to a recording?

938. Communication protocols: how will the team communicate?

939. What is the number of cases currently teamed?

940. Resource allocation: how will individual team members account for time and expenses, and how will this be allocated in the team budget?

941. What resources can be provided for the team in terms of equipment, space, time for training, protected time and space for meetings, and travel allowances?

942. Do you leverage technology engagement tools group chat, polls, screen sharing, etc.?

943. Must your team members rely on the expertise of other members to complete tasks?

944. What types of accommodations will be formulated and put in place for sustaining the team?

945. What are some potential sources of conflict among team members?

3.8 Team Performance Assessment: IBM InfoSphere DataStage

946. To what degree are the relative importance and priority of the goals clear to all team members?

947. Individual task proficiency and team process behavior: what is important for team functioning?

948. How hard did you try to make a good selection?

949. How do you encourage members to learn from each other?

950. To what degree can team members frequently and easily communicate with one another?

951. To what degree does the teams purpose constitute a broader, deeper aspiration than just accomplishing short-term goals?

952. What are you doing specifically to develop the leaders around you?

953. To what degree does the team possess adequate membership to achieve its ends?

954. If you have criticized someones work for method variance in your role as reviewer, what was the circumstance?

955. Can familiarity breed backup?

956. What makes opportunities more or less obvious?

957. Which situations call for a more extreme type of adaptiveness in which team members actually re-define roles?

958. Do friends perform better than acquaintances?

959. To what degree do members understand and articulate the same purpose without relying on ambiguous abstractions?

960. To what degree are fresh input and perspectives systematically caught and added (for example, through information and analysis, new members, and senior sponsors)?

961. To what degree will the team ensure that all members equitably share the work essential to the success of the team?

962. To what degree can all members engage in open and interactive considerations?

963. To what degree are sub-teams possible or necessary?

964. To what degree does the teams work approach provide opportunity for members to engage in results-based evaluation?

3.9 Team Member Performance Assessment: IBM InfoSphere DataStage

965. What are they responsible for?

966. What makes them effective?

967. New skills/knowledge gained this year?

968. How is assessment information achieved, stored?

969. What are the staffs preferences for training on technology-based platforms?

970. Do the goals support your organizations goals?

971. What happens if a team member receives a Rating of Unsatisfactory?

972. Are assessment validation activities performed?

973. What tools are available to determine whether all contract functional and compliance areas of performance objectives, measures, and incentives have been met?

974. What is the role of the Reviewer?

975. What are the standards or expectations for success?

976. What is the target group for instruction (e.g.,

individual and collective or small team instruction)?

977. How is your organizations Strategic Management System tied to performance measurement?

978. What are the basic principles and objectives of performance measurement and assessment?

979. Are the draft goals SMART ?

980. How does your team work together?

981. Does adaptive training work?

982. Why do performance reviews?

983. Did training work?

984. What does collaboration look like?

3.10 Issue Log: IBM InfoSphere DataStage

985. Do you often overlook a key stakeholder or stakeholder group?

986. How were past initiatives successful?

987. What is the stakeholders political influence?

988. Why do you manage human resources?

989. What date was the issue resolved?

990. Persistence; will users learn a work around or will they be bothered every time?

991. Why do you manage communications?

992. What is a Stakeholder?

993. What steps can you take for positive relationships?

994. Who reported the issue?

995. What does the stakeholder need from the team?

996. How do you reply to this question; you am new here and managing this major program. How do you suggest you build your network?

997. Is the issue log kept in a safe place?

998. Can an impact cause deviation beyond team, stage or IBM InfoSphere DataStage project tolerances?

999. Why multiple evaluators?

1000. Are stakeholder roles recognized by your organization?

4.0 Monitoring and Controlling Process Group: IBM InfoSphere DataStage

1001. Have operating capacities been created and/or reinforced in partners?

1002. What is the timeline for the IBM InfoSphere DataStage project?

1003. How to ensure validity, quality and consistency?

1004. How will staff learn how to use the deliverables?

1005. Change, where should you look for problems?

1006. Is it what was agreed upon?

1007. Is the schedule for the set products being met?

1008. Based on your IBM InfoSphere DataStage project communication management plan, what worked well?

1009. Is the verbiage used appropriate and understandable?

1010. How do you monitor progress?

1011. Is the program in place as intended?

1012. User: who wants the information and what are they interested in?

1013. How is agile IBM InfoSphere DataStage project management done?

1014. How well defined and documented were the IBM InfoSphere DataStage project management processes you chose to use?

1015. What do they need to know about the IBM InfoSphere DataStage project?

1016. What input will you be required to provide the IBM InfoSphere DataStage project team?

1017. How was the program set-up initiated?

4.1 Project Performance Report: IBM InfoSphere DataStage

1018. To what degree does the formal organization make use of individual resources and meet individual needs?

1019. What degree are the relative importance and priority of the goals clear to all team members?

1020. To what degree are the goals realistic?

1021. To what degree are the structures of the formal organization consistent with the behaviors in the informal organization?

1022. To what degree do team members understand one anothers roles and skills?

1023. To what degree do members articulate the goals beyond the team membership?

1024. To what degree do team members agree with the goals, relative importance, and the ways in which achievement will be measured?

1025. To what degree does the funding match the requirement?

1026. To what degree are the teams goals and objectives clear, simple, and measurable?

1027. Next Steps?

1028. To what degree will new and supplemental skills be introduced as the need is recognized?

1029. To what degree is there a sense that only the team can succeed?

1030. To what degree does the information network communicate information relevant to the task?

1031. To what degree does the teams approach to its work allow for modification and improvement over time?

1032. What is the degree to which rules govern information exchange between groups?

1033. To what degree does the teams purpose contain themes that are particularly meaningful and memorable?

1034. To what degree can the team ensure that all members are individually and jointly accountable for the teams purpose, goals, approach, and work-products?

4.2 Variance Analysis: IBM InfoSphere DataStage

1035. Are indirect costs charged to the appropriate indirect pools and incurring organization?

1036. How do you manage changes in the nature of the overhead requirements?

1037. Did an existing competitor change strategy?

1038. Who is generally responsible for monitoring and taking action on variances?

1039. Are meaningful indicators identified for use in measuring the status of cost and schedule performance?

1040. What business event caused the fluctuation?

1041. Contract line items and end items?

1042. What causes selling price variance?

1043. Do the rates and prices remain constant throughout the year?

1044. Are overhead cost budgets established for each department which has authority to incur overhead costs?

1045. Does the accounting system provide a basis for auditing records of direct costs chargeable to the contract?

1046. Does the scheduling system identify in a timely manner the status of work?

1047. Are the actual costs used for variance analysis reconcilable with data from the accounting system?

1048. Favorable or unfavorable variance?

1049. What types of services and expense are shared between business segments?

1050. Who are responsible for the establishment of budgets and assignment of resources for overhead performance?

1051. Are procedures for variance analysis documented and consistently applied at the control account level and selected WBS and organizational levels at least monthly as a routine task?

4.3 Earned Value Status: IBM InfoSphere DataStage

1052. Verification is a process of ensuring that the developed system satisfies the stakeholders agreements and specifications; Are you building the product right? What do you verify?

1053. If earned value management (EVM) is so good in determining the true status of a IBM InfoSphere DataStage project and IBM InfoSphere DataStage project its completion, why is it that hardly any one uses it in information systems related IBM InfoSphere DataStage projects?

1054. Are you hitting your IBM InfoSphere DataStage projects targets?

1055. Where is evidence-based earned value in your organization reported?

1056. When is it going to finish?

1057. How does this compare with other IBM InfoSphere DataStage projects?

1058. Where are your problem areas?

1059. Earned value can be used in almost any IBM InfoSphere DataStage project situation and in almost any IBM InfoSphere DataStage project environment. it may be used on large IBM InfoSphere DataStage projects, medium sized IBM InfoSphere DataStage projects, tiny IBM InfoSphere DataStage projects (in cut-down form), complex and simple IBM InfoSphere DataStage projects and in any market sector. some people, of course, know all about earned value, they have used it for years - but perhaps not as effectively as they could have?

1060. How much is it going to cost by the finish?

1061. What is the unit of forecast value?

1062. Validation is a process of ensuring that the developed system will actually achieve the stakeholders desired outcomes; Are you building the right product? What do you validate?

4.4 Risk Audit: IBM InfoSphere DataStage

1063. What are the commonly used work arounds in high risk areas?

1064. Is there a screening process that will ensure all participants have the fitness and skills required to safely participate?

1065. For this risk .. what do you need to stop doing, start doing and keep doing?

1066. Is your organization willing to commit significant time to the requirements gathering process?

1067. Are contracts reviewed before renewal?

1068. What effect would a better risk management program have had?

1069. Do industry specialists and business risk auditors enhance audit reporting accuracy?

1070. Has risk management been considered when planning an event?

1071. What impact does experience with one client have on decisions made for other clients during the risk-assessment process?

1072. Have risks been considered with an insurance

broker or provider and suitable insurance cover been arranged?

1073. What are the risks that could stop you from achieving your objectives?

1074. Is the number of people on the IBM InfoSphere DataStage project team adequate to do the job?

1075. Are there any forms the staff is required to sign?

1076. Are all managers or operators of the facility or equipment competent or qualified?

1077. What is the implication of budget constraint on this process?

1078. Tradeoff: how much risk can be tolerated and still deliver the products where they need to be?

1079. Does your organization have a register of insurance policies detailing all current insurance policies?

1080. What expertise do auditors need to generate effective business-level risk assessments, and to what extent do auditors currently possess the already stated attributes?

4.5 Contractor Status Report: IBM InfoSphere DataStage

1081. Who can list a IBM InfoSphere DataStage project as organization experience, your organization or a previous employee of your organization?

1082. What are the minimum and optimal bandwidth requirements for the proposed solution?

1083. What was the final actual cost?

1084. What was the actual budget or estimated cost for your organizations services?

1085. How long have you been using the services?

1086. What was the budget or estimated cost for your organizations services?

1087. How is risk transferred?

1088. What is the average response time for answering a support call?

1089. Describe how often regular updates are made to the proposed solution. Are corresponding regular updates included in the standard maintenance plan?

1090. What process manages the contracts?

1091. What was the overall budget or estimated cost?

1092. How does the proposed individual meet each requirement?

1093. If applicable; describe your standard schedule for new software version releases. Are new software version releases included in the standard maintenance plan?

1094. Are there contractual transfer concerns?

4.6 Formal Acceptance: IBM InfoSphere DataStage

1095. Was the client satisfied with the IBM InfoSphere DataStage project results?

1096. Does it do what IBM InfoSphere DataStage project team said it would?

1097. General estimate of the costs and times to complete the IBM InfoSphere DataStage project?

1098. Was the IBM InfoSphere DataStage project goal achieved?

1099. Have all comments been addressed?

1100. Was the IBM InfoSphere DataStage project work done on time, within budget, and according to specification?

1101. Do you buy-in installation services?

1102. Was business value realized?

1103. How does your team plan to obtain formal acceptance on your IBM InfoSphere DataStage project?

1104. What features, practices, and processes proved to be strengths or weaknesses?

1105. Who would use it?

1106. What was done right?

1107. Who supplies data?

1108. Does it do what client said it would?

1109. Is formal acceptance of the IBM InfoSphere DataStage project product documented and distributed?

1110. Was the sponsor/customer satisfied?

1111. What is the Acceptance Management Process?

1112. Did the IBM InfoSphere DataStage project manager and team act in a professional and ethical manner?

1113. Do you buy pre-configured systems or build your own configuration?

1114. How well did the team follow the methodology?

5.0 Closing Process Group: IBM InfoSphere DataStage

1115. What level of risk does the proposed budget represent to the IBM InfoSphere DataStage project?

1116. Does the close educate others to improve performance?

1117. Can the lesson learned be replicated?

1118. What areas were overlooked on this IBM InfoSphere DataStage project?

1119. How dependent is the IBM InfoSphere DataStage project on other IBM InfoSphere DataStage projects or work efforts?

1120. What is the IBM InfoSphere DataStage project Management Process?

1121. Did you do things well?

1122. Did the delivered product meet the specified requirements and goals of the IBM InfoSphere DataStage project?

1123. How critical is the IBM InfoSphere DataStage project success to the success of your organization?

1124. Were cost budgets met?

1125. What areas were overlooked on this IBM

InfoSphere DataStage project?

1126. How will you know you did it?

1127. What is the IBM InfoSphere DataStage project name and date of completion?

1128. Did the IBM InfoSphere DataStage project team have the right skills?

1129. How well did the chosen processes fit the needs of the IBM InfoSphere DataStage project?

1130. When will the IBM InfoSphere DataStage project be done?

5.1 Procurement Audit: IBM InfoSphere DataStage

1131. Is trend analysis performed on expenditures made by key employees and by vendor?

1132. Is the procurement process well organized?

1133. Are there procedures for trade-in arrangements?

1134. Is an appropriated degree of standardization of goods and services respected?

1135. Do you learn from benchmarking your own practices with international standards?

1136. Which contracts have been awarded for works, supply of products or provision of services?

1137. Are individuals with check-signing responsibility prohibited from signing blank checks?

1138. What are your procurement processes with contractors?

1139. Are there complementary rules to be used and are they applied?

1140. Are vendor price lists regularly updated?

1141. Was there a sound basis for the scorings applied to the criteria and was the scoring well balanced?

1142. When corresponding references were made, was a precise description of the performance not otherwise possible and were the already stated references accompanied by the words or equivalent?

1143. Who are the key suppliers?

1144. Are eu procurement regulations applicable?

1145. Are the internal control systems operational?

1146. Are controls proportionated to risks?

1147. Which are the main risks and controls of each phase?

1148. Are outsourcing and Public Private Partnerships considered as alternatives to in-house work?

1149. Did your organization calculate the contract value accurately?

1150. Did your organization decide upon an adequate and admissible procurement procedure?

5.2 Contract Close-Out: IBM InfoSphere DataStage

1151. What is capture management?

1152. Change in knowledge?

1153. Was the contract complete without requiring numerous changes and revisions?

1154. Parties: Authorized?

1155. How is the contracting office notified of the automatic contract close-out?

1156. Have all contracts been completed?

1157. Change in circumstances?

1158. Was the contract type appropriate?

1159. Parties: who is involved?

1160. Have all contracts been closed?

1161. Has each contract been audited to verify acceptance and delivery?

1162. Are the signers the authorized officials?

1163. How does it work?

1164. Have all acceptance criteria been met prior to

final payment to contractors?

1165. Was the contract sufficiently clear so as not to result in numerous disputes and misunderstandings?

1166. Why Outsource?

1167. Have all contract records been included in the IBM InfoSphere DataStage project archives?

1168. Change in attitude or behavior?

1169. What happens to the recipient of services?

1170. How/when used ?

5.3 Project or Phase Close-Out: IBM InfoSphere DataStage

1171. How much influence did the stakeholder have over others?

1172. What stakeholder group needs, expectations, and interests are being met by the IBM InfoSphere DataStage project?

1173. Was the schedule met?

1174. What were the actual outcomes?

1175. What advantages do the an individual interview have over a group meeting, and vice-versa?

1176. What was learned?

1177. Does the lesson educate others to improve performance?

1178. What were the desired outcomes?

1179. What is a Risk?

1180. In preparing the Lessons Learned report, should it reflect a consensus viewpoint, or should the report reflect the different individual viewpoints?

1181. Have business partners been involved extensively, and what data was required for them?

1182. What was expected from each stakeholder?

1183. Were risks identified and mitigated?

1184. What is this stakeholder expecting?

1185. Who is responsible for award close-out?

1186. Is the lesson based on actual IBM InfoSphere DataStage project experience rather than on independent research?

1187. Who exerted influence that has positively affected or negatively impacted the IBM InfoSphere DataStage project?

1188. What could be done to improve the process?

1189. What are the mandatory communication needs for each stakeholder?

5.4 Lessons Learned: IBM InfoSphere DataStage

1190. What are the needs of the individuals?

1191. How efficient and effective were meetings?

1192. What surprises did the team have to deal with?

1193. How many government and contractor personnel are authorized for the IBM InfoSphere DataStage project?

1194. How efficient were IBM InfoSphere DataStage project team meetings conducted?

1195. Are the lessons more complex and multivariate?

1196. What skills are required for the task?

1197. What were the success factors?

1198. What is the frequency of communication?

1199. Did the IBM InfoSphere DataStage project management methodology work?

1200. How actively and meaningfully were stakeholders involved in the IBM InfoSphere DataStage project?

1201. How efficient is the deliverable?

1202. Who had fiscal authority to manage the funding for the IBM InfoSphere DataStage project, did that work?

1203. What is your organizations performance history?

1204. How was the political and social history changed over the life of the IBM InfoSphere DataStage project?

1205. Was the control overhead justified?

1206. What are the Benefits of Measurements?

1207. How well do you feel the executives supported this IBM InfoSphere DataStage project?

1208. What is your strategy for data collection?

1209. Are there any hidden conflicts of interest?

Index

Made in the USA
Monee, IL
15 October 2022

15864685R00182